# FEARLESS
## in *Heels*™

*Powerful*
*Potential Purpose*
PUBLISHING

www.ppp-publishing.com

ISBN: 978-1-7376603-4-7

Published by Powerful Potential & Purpose Publishing.
Book and cover design by Allison Chick.

Printed in the United States of America.

First printing edition 2021.

*To those who lost their lives to domestic violence.*

*To the heroes who heal victims and survivors.*

*To the warriors who fight alongside me against domestic violence.*

# *Table of Contents*

## *Young Frankie*

## *Frankie, Esquire*

# *Preface*

## *Fearless, In Heels*
### *Fighting abuse, for them and for me.*

"Times Up"- take your fucking hands off me!

As a college student, I survived domestic violence at the hands of a boyfriend.

As a law student, I endured sexual harassment by a classmate.

As a new attorney, I endured inequality in the work place.

I say "No More" to domestic violence and abuse.

My name is Frankie, and this is the story. I rose from victim of domestic violence to victor and transformed my life. I became an attorney-advocate to fight for others.

Kathy Piperno, Esq., kept a secret for thirty years. Through real life stories and fictionalized characters and events, Frankie takes you on a journey of what it is like to live with domestic violence.

Some say I am the heroine in a real-life drama. I say, I took my power back and I pay it forward.

# *Young Frankie*

### Chapter One
### The Good Girl

*All he did was complain, balking at everything, high
as a kite while she placed her palms over her ears. She could
not stand the screaming any longer. The sun setting with
beautiful magenta, pinks and orange and all her fears, would
she survive the night? Would he ever die and get out of my
life once and for all? It may sound ruthless, but I hope the
pressure on his neck is increased until his last breath is stolen.*

"I'll break your legs if you're not a good girl,"

Welcome to my family. A mixture of craziness, fun
and caring in their own way. The supper table was not always
the most joyous times and more stressful than one could
imagine. Even though the meals were to die for that mom
and Grandma cooked for the family dinners. It could take
hours or even days to prepare some of the amazing dishes that

sometimes can get thrown across the table, landing on your lap. Especially, if you didn't follow the rules. Always the rules, which by the way we didn't always understand. I'll break your legs, the words she still hears in her head and didn't understand.

Frankie was always scared, surviving on high alert, anxious and determined to please. She learned to be fearless or pretend to be because one day it would come in handy. She and her two sisters, raised in a first-generation Italian, Catholic family, enjoyed the family festivities and learned about respect daily. Her parents worked hard for everything they had. If they didn't respect them, there were consequences. Dad's mom was born in Italy and known as the "Golden Child," the one who could do no wrong. The kids had to put up with "her ways." Love was measured by food and her post war grandparents provided the best they knew. The expectations were high and occasionally it was simpler to hide and be silent than engage in anything for fear of being wrong. There are all kinds of trauma and abuse, Frankie would understand one day, but she never considered this to be one of them.

Frankie was the odd one out, you might say. Actually, she wasn't like anybody in her neighborhood. Constantly the sassy one and arguing, "Boys and girls are equal" while others made fun of her, sought to intimidate and bully her. Thoughts would frequently wander through her brain, speculating if her parents adopted her because she deemed herself the black sheep. She didn't look like the fair haired, fair skinned sisters with her dark brown hair and deep brown eyes. She felt different and generally not acknowledged. She just wanted to be understood, to get the spotlight and be embraced and acknowledged. Would it ever come? Perhaps Frankie would find it within her own journey, one day.

The family settled in an Italian neighborhood in what they call row homes situated just a few blocks from the convent. There was no privacy. You could hear through the walls. Screaming, yelling and even an occasional dish being thrown could be heard, but no one ever mentioned those secrets. All family matters were confidential, no one discussed anything. Yes, denial was customary. There was judgement, however, by neighbors. One could feel and experience it in their glances. They especially liked to criticize the young ladies when they wore makeup and gaudy clothing. They peeped out their windows and being certain to gossip to someone "She's a whore." They might even yell out the window, "I'm a gonna tell your father!" Shaking their fists in the air, they established what was appropriate. The young girls rushed by quickly and giggled later.

Sister Fatima, Sister Onorina, and Sister Lucia monitored the youngsters as they walked by their homes every afternoon. Frankie was always on guard and didn't wish to disappoint them or get in trouble. She was sure they had a direct connection with God and would condemn her in a blink. Good grief, how do they wear those funny things on their head and live in black all the time? she wondered. A habit they called it. Who gave it that name? While other young girls were dreaming about being chosen as the May Queen in honor of Mother Mary, Frankie had other things on her mind and wanted nothing to do with it.

Mom consistently restrained her voice. She never raised an eyebrow or her tone, quite complacent in most situations. She was the dutiful wife. Frankie often wondered why she was so silent. One learned not to pressure her too far, or else. The wooden spoon might float across the room in slow motion. It was aimed for your head if you sassed your parents. Duck, the girls would giggle, avoiding the fierce attempt to knock them out as they ran from the room. She noticed dad was silent at the dinner table, occasionally nodding. It was hard to know what was going on in his head. However, when he did have something to say it could very well be in anger and verbally abusive.

Frankie observed more than others, quite entertained by the personality traits of each family member, the noisy neighbors, the street bullies, and the cute guys in school. One day I will have it all and live happily ever after, she fantasized.

It was a muggy Sunday, beads of perspiration on her neck as she knelt on the solid wood, praying to God and listening to the priest. He would raise his hands, eyes piercing and conveying the sermon. Wondering if she was terrible and committed a sin, would they stone her to death? Memories of these days haunted her for years as the incense fog swirled around, inducing a cough. She gave her finest to be the good girl and feared going to hell. I wonder if people live in this fear all over the earth. Oh, the questions Frankie had on her brain, even as a young girl, would continue throughout her life. I think I will read the Cinderella story again. One day that will be me, she daydreamed.

The alarm blasted Monday morning, as mom would call out, "Wake up sleepy head, time for school." Pulling the sheets over her head for just five more minutes, she prayed she would reach the expectations of her dad and get straight 'A's on her exams today. Please God, help me so I don't go to hell. It became an obsession with Frankie to overachieve, to be popular and make her dreams come true. Surely dad would smack her upside her head if she ever smoked or drank and don't dare kiss a boy. These core values go deeper than she would comprehend and provide a sense of tenacity needed later in life. Who knew? After a quick bowl of cereal, she put on her uniform, gathered her books, and walked to school. The rules were stringent, and you either behaved or went to the principal's office to get reprimanded.

"Bye mom," receiving a nod and a little wave.

The dreaded time of year was coming around. It was May, and the girls wished to be crowned Queen. Frankie wanted no part. A brief thought floated through her head. "What if I was the queen and proved to dad I am a good girl. Would he respect me?"

Much to her astonishment, she would indeed get elected May Queen. Standing in front of her mirror she proclaimed, *"I, Frankie, the queen, shall choose my court, parade down the street and prove to everyone who I am."* But it never seemed entirely sufficient. Her intention was to stand out, be worthy and valued.

God had a different court in mind for her one day. One wonders if Frankie realized the power in those words she spoke and where it would lead her in life.

Frankie earned the chance to wear a white lace gown with puffy sleeves. It was like a wedding dress with white gloves and a crown made of carnations and a blue ribbon. The court, young women in pastel-colored gowns, carrying small colorful bouquets, the boys in suits and ties with polished black shoes paraded as they led her past the convent and neighbors to the statue of the Blessed Virgin Mary. Big Angie stood there, gaping at Frankie, envious because she presumed, they would inaugurate her the May Queen. Perhaps she should have gone to church every Sunday and abstained from kissing the boys to get votes. Frankie smirked walking past her. The nuns all beamed and looked pleased and perhaps finally she would gain the respect she sought and go to heaven, too.

I do not want dad to break my legs and surely, he must be proud of me now, gracefully walking; she thought. They always followed the yearly ritual with a party, and that was the best part. Frankie loved her pizza and was excited about her court. Her friends and family members would party soon. Well, at least once I can remove this uncomfortable dress, she mumbled in her head. Dad never said a word except "stand up tall."

It's over and we can dance now. She ran up the stairs to her bedroom, flung off the fancy white dress and blasted the dance music. Frankie had a passion for dance since she walked. She would wiggle and giggle and shake her body. It always made her happy and everyone else laugh. Mom had everything prepared, always attentive to every detail as she quietly and dutifully prepared all the food, plates, and simple decorations.

Disco music, time to party, they danced the night away.

Each Saturday morning, the aroma of garlic and olive oil permeated their home. Meatballs rolled, browning and then tossed in the gravy. Yes, Gravy, not sauce! Don't be stunad! Frankie visualized her dad shaking his fingers. Even years later, speaking those words randomly, she always wondered would he think she was stupid. Surely, she was not. She was smart. He must have just liked the phrase as it eloquently flowed off his tongue. Dad had a good deal of slang words. She could never repeat them if she wanted to remain a good girl. Little did she know one day she would emulate her father's vernacular when her own frustrations were out of control.

*One day she would learn about generational trauma, and it carried forward in families.*

The windows open, neighbors calling up to us "Smells good," as they walked home from the local Italian bakery. Saturdays were a little boisterous in the neighborhood. Everyone scurried around to prepare for the main Sunday meal. One of Frankie's favorite things was the smell of freshly baked bread, crisp crusts and soaking it in the gravy. Her plate had more gravy than pasta and the taste of garlic, tomatoes, basil and a little dash of this and that had her salivating. Her mouth wide open to touch her tongue with the drenched bread, "Frankie, eat your pasta too," her mom would urge.

Mom would send Frankie to the bakery as her weekly chore. However, she often returned home having eaten half the loaf. Wiggling her index finger, mom would declare, "Now you go get another loaf and don't devour it this time." Eventually, she gave her daughter the specific amount of change for two loaves of bread. There was no stopping her from biting the one, her mom realized. Occasionally, the nice Italian lady at the bakery would give Frankie a little sample of the homemade Italian lemon ice with real lemons. An array of pastries and breads were tough to resist, but oh, that lemon ice was yummy.

"Turn the gravy and don't let it burn," mom shouted. "Are you daydreaming again, Frankie?" Meatballs and gravy were a serious business and every mother on the block boasted about my mom's. They were the best because she chose quality cheese, fresh basil and sometimes added ground pork to the beef.

"Throw in an onion to soak up the grease, Frankie."

Grandma shouted from the other room. "Ok, I will," but most times she forgot. Salivating, as the smell alone can make you drool, Frankie would sneak a bite. Mom wanted to slap her hand slightly, shaking those fingers again. "No, No," giggling as she grabbed the other half from Frankie's hand and finished it up. "Squisito," she gave her approval, kissing her fingers up to God.

Dinner was always served promptly at the exact time every day and you better not be late. We set the table with our Sunday linen napkins, which were not supposed to get dirty. Go figure. Mom always had her apron on while dad took his seat like a king at the head of the table. There was a special wine glass too and after our blessing he sipped it like the priest at Mass, offering it up to God. Mom gave Frankie and her sisters a stern look, motioning to the linen napkin to place it on their lap. Subtly rolling her eyes over to dad as if we should be frightened of him if we forgot. Quickly, Frankie opened the napkin and placed it diligently on her lap, so her legs didn't get broken. Not going to happen today if I can avoid it, thoughts floated in her head. Everyone was quiet, just waiting.

"Mangia!" We grabbed our forks and twirled our spaghetti, which was difficult for any kid. "More cheese anyone?" Mom would provide it whether we wanted it or not. It was a nervous habit. Every time Frankie would start a sentence, mom would say, "Eat the meatball, Frankie." Frankie just wanted to show Dad her report card so he would be proud of her 'A's. Those eyes stared across the table and with no words, Frankie knew to keep her mouth shut. Her sisters bowed their heads dutifully while carefully twirling their spaghetti like ladies. I just wanted to tell him I made the all-star team for softball. Maybe later, when I could sit near him after dinner, no one would shut me up. Dinner was done and in silence, we all knew our positions to wash, dry, and put away the dishes. Mom always looked tired. Dad sat in front of the TV. Frankie did not get the attention she desired to chat with dad. He was too busy engaged in his program.

Frankie's parents assumed she could handle herself, so she did her best to do so. She would not fail at anything. Sporting her t-shirt that shouted, "I can beat any boy on the block." Little did she know she would beat many things in life.

Those rotten boys laughed at her, challenged her until she beat them at their own game. Most of the girls were jealous when she outdid the boys in box ball, horseshoes, wiffle ball and even neighborhood spats. DeeDee, the bully, showed up to pick on the little kids and decided one day to mess with Frankie. She snatched the wiffle ball bat little Mikey was holding, jumped on top of him. Frankie defended the little boy and knocked DeeDee to the ground. Mikey stood there crying. It broke Frankie's soft heart and made her more determined to make him smile when she returned the bat. Defending others was something she grew to do over the years when anyone was bullied.

*It came naturally.*

This was only the beginning of many battles. Pudgy
G.G. scheduled a pre-arranged fist fight over the boy she
liked, Tony. She thought Frankie wanted him. The park was
the scene and the neighborhood kids gathered around. It was
like a scene from "The West Side Story." Some wanted to
see Pudgy knocked down on her fat ass while others cheered
on Frankie. "Don't let her get you down," Jay shouted, her
best buddy. "You won't get up if she sits on you."

Frankie fell to the ground when she lost her balance.
One of the other kids threw something on the ground, which
distracted her, while Pudgy went to punch Frankie in the
face. Thank God Jay was there to break up the fight. With
a bloody nose from the punch, she and Jay walked home.
"Good fight, Frankie. Let's get you cleaned up." Jay was a
protector, and he also had no tolerance for cheating pricks
and bullies.

Over the next few years, Frankie would have to
enlist some help to back her up. When Rita confronted her
down an alley, throwing rocks at her she knew she needed a
plan. All the other jealous cocky girls wanted to take Frankie
out. It was hard growing up not having real friends, except
Jay.

The day came that changed it all. Now in 9th grade,
a pack of three bullies followed her down a cold, long
dark stairwell. Joey had a crush on Frankie. Little did they
know, Joey belonged to no one. He was a cheating fool and
Frankie had no interest. As Frankie headed to Algebra class,

the three stooges stood at the top of the stairs, peering down upon her. Punching their fists, left into right, like a gang movie.

Confident and snarky "Really girls, you can have him," she declared as she slowly backed out of the dark hallway with one eye over her shoulder, thinking "holy shit." She now learned a strategy and would learn how to make deals.

Foul mouthed, skinny Cookie needed help with math, and Frankie made her a deal. She realized people were afraid of people like Cookie . Now Frankie could safely walk the halls and focus on the Honor Society and Student Government without fear of a black eye or bloody nose. Cookie would pass math.

On graduation day, a sunny and warm June morning, they all gathered in the amphitheater. She was thrilled to wear her Honor Society sash, accepted a college scholarship, and received her "All Public" award from her softball coach. It was time now to leave all the bullies behind and head to college.

*The fight of her life was ahead of her and in Frankie Fashion, she would fearlessly walk into her power.*

## *Chapter 2*
### Through the Fire

*Friday and Saturday nights Frankie broke her own rules.*
*Times had shifted now that she had her sovereignty, and she*
*wished to experience the world and meet her love.*
*This would begin a secret she would carry for*
*thirty years.*

She didn't dare approach any men during "Ladies Choice." Assuming her position on the right side of the disco floor near the bar, she waited for "Gentlemen's Choice." She hoped he would want her. Most girls dream of that one, handsome dude they spot across the room and imagine he will be the one. Frankie was no different.

The disco ball reflected twinkling light on the wooden floor while couples danced to tunes of *Saturday Night Fever's*, *"Stayin' Alive."* She listened to the words,

*"I've been kicked around since I was born and now it's alright, it's okay."* Standing on her heels, appearing taller than her petite five feet 2 inches, glowing, her heart pounding to meet him. *"You can tell by the way I use my walk I'm a woman's man, no time to talk. Life going nowhere, somebody help me. I'm stayin' alive."* No truer words would be her motto one day battling to stay alive.

Relying on her superficial criteria, she danced with a handful of contenders, mainly because she loved dancing. None of them were 'marriage material.' They were all "players." It was her buddy, Jay, who instructed her how to do the hustle and do new line dances. She was ready for the nightclubs. The hometown disco mimicked Studio 54 in New York with strobe lights, fog mist rising from the floor, all mixed with the scent of cigarettes and cologne. Exhilarated and cocky on the surface, nervous on the inside, standing by for the chance to fall in love. Yes, it was raining men! Hallelujah!

It was 1985 and Frankie had the big, updo hair, huge earrings and high heels. He wore a grey "Members Only" jacket, tight jeans, gel on his thick, slicked back hair and pointy shoes. He was hot. Frankie's eyes roamed and there he stood, tall, dark, suave, wearing a heavy gold chain. The childhood bullies were gone. She was on the prowl for her prospective partner.

Oh dear, he's coming closer. Will he ask me to dance? Her heart pounding through her chest as he clutched her sweaty hand with his warm, solid grip.

OMG, OMG, it's happening! Tall and confident, he drew his woman to the dancefloor. The whiff of Drakkar cologne had her drooling and fantasizing about him. She gazed up, mesmerized. He picked me! Her brain could not quiet down. Will he want me? Will I get to kiss him? Is he going to be my sweetheart?

The DJ switched the song, *"Through the Fire."* He pulled her closer to his muscular body, claiming her with his firm touch. He leaned over, stroking her cheek against his, after hours of dancing and whispered, "Can I have your phone number?" There was something about him. He wasn't like the cheaters she had been with previously. Magic it was! They went on dancing to *"It's ladies' night and the feelings right."* It must be a sign! The song was over, they held hands and went over to the bouncer and requested a pen. Nervously, Frankie wrote her number on his palm, not actually expecting to hear from him again. He brushed her tenderly on the cheek after a long, tiresome, but exhilarating night of dancing as they went home. He was a charmer, no doubt.

Tossing and turning, there was no way Frankie was going to get a sound sleep. Like most girls, she had a fantasy, and it was rolling through her mind all night. Will he, won't he? Like pulling the petals from a daisy, Will he love me? Will he not? One by one, she had run all the excuses through her head. She was not worthy of this gorgeous, hot hunk. He is probably a player too. My parents will never allow me to date him. Stop it! she screamed in her head. I'm smart and pretty and I deserve my prince charming. Shut up stupid, the other sarcastic voice in her mumbled. You can't keep a man. No clue girlie, how to attract the right one. Frankie cried, worthless and distraught.

Morning came quickly, exhausted and frazzled, she anxiously prayed, he would call. The hours lagged on all day, like a never-ending fairy tale. Then she gave up. She had to stay focused.

Slick was his name, and that should have been a clue to the character of this stud. Frankie didn't care. He called later that evening and her hands trembled as he said, "Hey babe, want to get together tonight?" The words could not leave her lips quick enough, and she surely didn't want to sound like a schoolgirl. "I believe I can make that work." Frankie was nervous. Do I let him know where I live? No. I can't take that risk, especially after all the jerks I have attracted in the past. I'm a good girl and don't want to look like easy prey. "I will meet you at the club, ok?" "It's a deal, doll."

Holy Crap! I can't fucking believe it, she screeched. He asked me for a date! Nonstop, she obsessed in her head, dancing around the house. What will I wear? Swinging open the closet door, she pulled out all her dresses, throwing them on the bed one by one. Nope, wrong color, too sexy, not sexy enough. Will he like this? The clock was ticking fast.

She threw off her clothes and jumped into a hot shower to freshen up thinking, I should take a cold shower.

The only thing Frankie was certain of at this point was her choice of heels. I need the highest ones because I'm a foot smaller than him. These will work, she thought, as she slipped them on her petite feet. The purple dress! That's what I will wear. Purple became a very special color for Frankie and later in life she would learn its significance. Right now, she just wanted to look hot and alluring, but cautious not to overstimulate her stud. Ha! Grabbing her purse, she headed to the club.

*Breathe Frankie!*

Slick stood charmingly at the entrance to the club when Frankie saw him. Slick was the perfect name, she thought, because his hair was always slicked back with gel. His eyes caught hers and she melted. He took a step towards her, reached out his hand like a gentleman, and together they walked onto the dance floor like a couple who danced lifetimes together. It's so easy.

Everyone watched, enthralled by their connection, including her work partner, Dick, who she noticed tonight. They took over the dance floor. Frankie had the attention she always desired. He wrapped his hand around her tiny waist, slipping it down a little further with each dance, turning her on. She remained calm. I'm a good girl, she repeated in her head, inconspicuously stopping his hand from going lower.

*"Celebration"* came on! He twirled her around, her dress slightly flared out and beaming with a happy smile on

her face. It became their song and a memorable night. They were cool! Yahoo! Celebrate good times! C'mon! Frankie waved her hand to her friends, inviting them to party along. She wanted everyone to have fun with them. The gang all smiled and joined the happy couple. It was the beginning of many passionate nights. It was the night Frankie fell in love. Laughing and partying together, Frankie felt loved. While it lasted.

Her dreamboat was six-foot-two, and a photographer. She felt they were living the perfect lives, like the TV show "*Happy Days.*" One of his friends even reminded her of the character, Chachi. On weekends, the gang would pack into one of their cars, checking for "easy" girls. Eventually, they made the rounds. Once Slick and Frankie became an item, his best friends dated Frankie's friends. There was Tommy, the funniest, who made them all laugh. Markie was the artist, always asking the girls to pose nude. The girls always refused, so thought Frankie. She did pose once for a beautiful black-and-white photo, which was shoved into her nightstand. Another secret she kept close. Evenings meant kissing outside, piling into the car to drive home, laughing, snuggling and on cloud nine. Years later, she learned several of the girls did pose nude, keeping it secret.

Dad hated Slick, but he hated all her boyfriends, so that was nothing new. Grandma spied on them from the third-floor window, as she didn't trust any of them. It didn't matter they were in their early twenties. Her mom always made sweet tea, being kind and making everyone comfortable. Chuckling in her head, Frankie often waited for her mom to say, "Want a meatball, anyone?"

"Frankie, watch out for that boy," Grandma said every night. "I don't trust him." "C'mon Grandma, he is awesome, and he loves me!" She would roll her eyes and kiss her rosary up to God.

The *Jordache* jeans got tighter, perfume spritzed, and *Candies* were rocking her feet. She was in style, sexy, and felt like a queen, a disco queen. Slick's parents never welcomed her. Often, she wondered why, but hoped they would change their mind one day. Tucking in her gold crucifix between her breasts, she ran down the steps to meet Slick. His friends waited in their shiny car! The gang was ready to party, and Grandma was peeking out the window shaking her head. The judgements were everywhere. Why is it people assume, she questioned?

Tonight, was the night. Slick had bought Frankie a gift. After a slow dance, his warm, wet lips caressed her mouth as she shivered. They had been dating for months, dancing the night away, and neither one expressed their feelings for each other. The young couple had not consummated their affections for each other and, of course, Frankie was not ready. Grandma would surely know. Dad would probably kill her. It would not happen; she swore. Slowly he put his arms around her, slipping a delicate gold necklace with a heart on her neck, whispering "I love you." Her legs quivered. She was speechless, surprised. It was the happiest moment of her life. Everyone observed the couple, envious of their love. The disco queen was in heaven. She knew many would not approve. "I'm the happiest I've been. I don't give a shit what others think." Frankie had a glow about her all night as she danced. Slick's good looks were admired by all.

Slick was protective of his woman, always guarding her wherever they went. They enjoyed going to concerts because she loved music and museums. He loved art. He wanted her to see the world with him, holding her close to his side. She felt safe in his arms, trusting he was hers forever. Unbeknownst to her, the girls in the neighborhood called him "Rico Suave," like the song. The guys called him the "Player," always consumed with romance. He once said, "I'm very sexual," Frankie responded, "I'm very Catholic and I don't know what you are talking about."

So caught up in her imaginary world and fantasy of a married life, she never realized what was going on around her. Naïve, she believed everything Slick told her, ignoring the signs and cautions Grandma continually blurted out. "Frankie, that boy is not good enough for you. He will hurt you!" "Ok, Grandma, I will be smart and careful." As usual, Grandma shook her head, kissed the crucifix on her necklace and offered a prayer to God. It was a busy week at school with exams and a part-time job when Frankie came home exhausted. Kicking off her heels, swollen and sore feet, she plopped on her bed and wondering "Is Grandma right?" "Frankie," a call came from mom in the kitchen. "Frankie, come eat. I made some food for you." "Ok mom." It was always mom's way of soothing anything. Perhaps she was concerned about Frankie's relationship. "Invite your friends over Frankie for dinner soon." "Yeah, ok mom." Typically, the gang hung out at Frankie's as it was one of the largest row homes and everyone loved mom's tea. Grandma would subtly, not so subtly, tap on the window if she caught any of us kissing.

As usual, Frankie was consumed with getting 'A's in college. She wanted to graduate with honors. Graduation day came soon, and they stood under the large, white party tent on the front lawn of the campus. Slick was nowhere to be found. His excuse was no car. He was a struggling artist. Grandma shook her head again, this time with a soft grunt. Frankie didn't dare show her disappointment, but it was in her heart.

The commencement speaker, a female attorney, spoke passionately of opportunities, recognition and successes women in the 80s were experiencing. Frankie craved recognition, the pomp and circumstance. She had earned her Associate's Degree in Business Administration, and was proud of the achievement. Though it was an unfamiliar experience, she knew she deserved and earned it.

That very day, Frankie made a decision, one which would change the course of her life. The next day, she found a job ad on the college bulletin. Immediately she contacted the woman, Kat, for an interview and accepted the position as manager of her boutique.

"Mom, I got the job! I'm going to be a manager!"
"That's nice, Frankie," was all she heard. Deflated, she felt she could never gain recognition. Is this abuse or humility? She wondered.

The gang rented a beach house together. Frankie really needed a little time to rejuvenate after school and before she began her new job. It sounded like fun and all eight of them said "Yes." Some girls would stay all summer and the guys came down on weekends. Jay rented a small place next to the large beach house to keep an eye on Frankie. He adored her, but she rarely noticed. After a few fun days, the entire scene became an epic failure, at least for Frankie. Jay was aware of what Slick was doing and warned Frankie of his escapades with his ex-girlfriend. In fact, all the guys were cheating. "How could they?" Frankie was distraught, depressed and angry. "Fuckin A, I'm done!" Her friend even confirmed he was cheating. "That's it! No one makes a fool of me!"

Slick was as cool as his name. He said he couldn't help himself. He was enticed and lost control. "I'm a man. It happens Frankie," trying to convince her he was innocent of his actions. "Please, please don't leave me Frankie, I love you." She now had the upper hand and control over him, like a child begging for mercy for knocking over the lamp; he hoped she would forgive this as an oversight.

Markie and Chachi found Frankie later, begging her to

stay with Slick. "You are the best thing for him. Even though he is a cheating bastard. He loves you Frankie, and he says he can't live  without you!" The begging continued for days. He may want to marry the good girl, but I will be damned if marrying a good-looking guy means I have to tolerate this abuse. Frankie should have left and run from the drama and manipulation that was waiting for her. She didn't.

Slick was slick alright, and he charmed Frankie back into his life, vowing his love and loyalty to her. She wanted to believe him, so she did. It's difficult to let go of loving someone.

Grandma got wind of what happened. Fights, screaming and begging for understanding followed. Mom would prep meals to soothe Frankie's heart and soul. Unapproving, the family shunned the relationship, making Frankie more determined to prove them wrong. Sometimes, you can win and some you will lose. This one she wanted to win. The evidence was there, but the circumstances were not clear to her. Soon it would become very clear.

It was their anniversary. Slick arranged a romantic candlelight dinner. He was sharing a slice of cheesecake with his date, feeding her seductively, when he grabbed the napkin. He drew an engagement ring. It was a beautiful design, and it thrilled Frankie. Maybe he will finally propose to her. She had lots of wedding plans and her dress already picked out. All he had to do was ask. "What do you think of this design?" Of course, she loved it. It was a tease. She will play along.

Frankie got to the disco earlier than usual. She had to brag a little about the impending engagement. The happiest gal alive, she twirled around the floor. The glittering disco lights made her dizzy when she spotted Slick…hugging another woman. They locked eyes as she stood still. I must be hallucinating. Her beautiful smile turned into a frown as he sheepishly approached Frankie. Tears in his eyes, he said, "She loves me more and I am marrying her." Mortified, she couldn't move. She froze.

The DJ blasted, *"She Dropped a Bomb on Me,"* when someone grabbed her hand to bring her to the dancefloor. Her head tilted back, glaring at Slick, wanting to choke him.

Frankie's eyes clouded with tears, crushed so deeply. She didn't realize whose chest she was leaning into while crying on their shirt. Once she became composed, the scent of Obsession reminded her of Dick, from the mall. Relieved a bit and shielded from the humiliation, she held him tight. The song ended and exhausted, Frankie wanted to go home. Feeling ambushed by Slick, she wondered who he was marrying. Dick walked her to the car. "Get some sleep. I'll see you at work tomorrow. How about I treat you to chicken parmesan for lunch?" He kissed her forehead, and she nodded thanks.

Pounding her feet up the concrete steps to the front door, she had to hide Grandma's predictions. Brokenhearted was an understatement. The bastard didn't bother to pick up any of her calls from the payphones on her way home. The coward took his rotary phone off the hook! Frankie was in no mood to hear "I warned you." She already felt stunad and ashamed. This was not over by a long shot. She huffed and blew her nose.

Dick was open to hear all the gossip, he actually ate it up. He was like a shark circling in a tank, preying on every word and emotion. Frankie noticed nothing while she ranted. The chicken parmesan was tasty and Frankie was the delicacy. Frankie soon learned from Slick's friends he was screwing around with Lucy. Everyone apparently knew her heart was broken. A close friend of Slick's told Frankie "You were his first love, and he will have regrets."

That seemed to satisfy her enough to search for healing and a new life.

*Chapter 3*
Strangled, Not Choked

*Boxed in by a judge on one side and a law clerk on the other,*
*Frankie heard in slow motion from the guest speaker, she was*
*strangled, not choked.*

"She abandoned me and left me with strangers," he reveals,
sobbing on the floor.

Dick's parents were attorneys and powerful advocates
for social justice. Educated and wealthy defenders of the
Constitution, they took their self-appointed roles seriously.
Neither had a violent bone in their body. They yearned for a
child and adopted Dick as an infant. He never talked of his
birth parents until Frankie tried to understand the monster he
became once she moved to California.

He was good to her, showered her with gifts and gave
her attention except for that 'one' time. Surely, he wouldn't do
it again, she swore.

Kat was moving to San Francisco and closing all of her New York stores. She offered Frankie a management position after she showed her worth as a boutique manager. Without hesitancy, Frankie jumped at the opportunity. Now, with trepidation, she had to reveal her intention to Dick and pay the price if he didn't like the news. The decision to leave came swiftly. She figured they would establish a new life, and Frankie hoped for a better one. They had been dancing and dating for a while and perhaps the relationship was ready for a new direction. Besides, she didn't want to move alone.

After pizza night at Dick's home, Frankie bragged about Kat's offer, expecting he would celebrate with her. She leaned in to kiss him goodnight when he forced her into a choke-hold, raised her up by the neck, her feet dangling, and flung her against his closet door. Her body crashed hard and then slumped to the floor. It threw her into shock. Dick had never been violent before, just a pothead who couldn't get his shit together.

Through snot and spit, he verbally attacked Frankie, screaming, "You're nothing. I created you, and you're not leaving me!" Dick was desperate to stop Frankie from leaving him, his manner of keeping her to himself. His way of saying "I will kill you so I can keep you."

Freaked out and wide-eyed, she endured the assault until he was satisfied. She received the message, and he discharged the death grip around her throat. She realized she would never escape. In shock, frozen, terror raced through her veins, and severe pain consumed her body and her thoughts. As Dick chastised her, Frankie pulled herself up, rubbed off his spit and broke down. He shouted, "You made me do it." "You were going to abandon me just like she did," he cried quietly in the corner.

"Go to hell," she sighed under her breath, scarcely able to speak. How the hell did I force him to do it?

Enraged, Frankie thought, "You will pay for this. No one strikes me, not since the fistfights with the guys in the neighborhood." Frankie demanded, "It's over." She dashed to the car, hit the gas and drove down Dick's front lawn. Adrenaline was pumping so fast, fear mixed with hysteria. She hardly saw through the windshield or fog as she prayed. Alone with her thoughts, "No one saw him choke me." Her secret was never to be made public. Secrets were not shared growing up and denial was an easier place to live, it implied. Focus Frankie, focus.

The harrowing 20-minute race home seemed like hours. She crashed into a bush, scraping the surface of her car as she pulled into her driveway of her parents' home. Fearful he may have followed her or called her parents, she jumped out, raced inside, hoping no one would see her. Down the cellar steps, she found and grabbed a mirror to check for "evidence" on her neck and face, handprints, fingerprints and black and blue marks. Thank God there was nothing to indicate Dick's brutal attack, no ligature marks, and no witnesses to his crime. No need to call the police because her secret was safe! Huffing, unable to slow down her breath, she bent over slightly, grasped her face, and sobbed quietly. Pull yourself together, girl, and get upstairs.

Quietly creeping up the stairs, she deliberately opened the door, slithered into bed, attempting to slow her breathing and calm down. She nudged her face into the pillow, curled over and cried herself to sleep. It shattered her heart again, but not her spirit. Frankie didn't understand any of this. How can someone treat you affectionately, buy presents, take you to dinner and state they choose you; only to try to murder you. It was all so bewildering.

The phone rang incessantly the following day, each time Frankie hung up. "Who's that?" Grandma called out. "Wrong number." Dick was not about to quit and ultimately triumphed over Frankie's little sister. The blond-haired, blue-eyed baby became sick of hearing the phone ring. She shoved it in her sister's face. "Poor Dick, he loves you." Frankie was not free yet.

Tormented by his calls, he won Frankie over too. She caved in, because she was frightened to be alone in California and he alleged he loved her. He couldn't bear to be without her. Her intention was to be rich and famous and prepared everything to preserve her confidence and self-respect. Dragging Dick with her to San Francisco, like a heavy rock, Kat was pissed.

Kat noticed Frankie's messy breakup with Slick had pressured her into the arms of Dick. 30 years later, Frankie would recognize Kat threw her the first lifeline, an escape from

Dick, but she didn't take it.

It was a dream come true for Frankie. A beautiful
estate with a lemon grove, a view of the ocean, and "A
private suite for me–I mean, for us." Kat glared at him before
she took off for the holidays, but she couldn't shake him.
Something was terribly wrong.

During their stay, Frankie and Dick toured the city,
hunted for apartments and searched the local restaurants.
Dick raided the refrigerator, rented Blockbuster videos
and enjoyed takeout food, dropping his crap everywhere.
He seemed very unappreciative, similar to the absence of
gratitude he had for his adoptive parents. He punished his
parents every day for his mother's decision. Frankie hoped he
would not repeat this pattern.

Excited to pick up applications for apartments,
Frankie also came upon the local college. She would attend
and graduate with a degree. Her goal was to be like Kat, wear
expensive clothes, drive a Jaguar, and acquire millions. Dick
would not ruin it, even if she had to endure further pain.

Dick sickened her. She sat in that beautiful suite with
ugly Dick, whose rage and brokenness poisoned everyone and
everything he touched. His pot smoking was out of control,
his lack of consideration for property and vulgarity grew each
day. The apartment was small and smelled of marijuana. The
garbage smelled because the loser couldn't even get up to take
it out. The refrigerator was empty, except for a few bottles of
beer.

The violent "choke-hold" was Dick's ultimate show of power and control. A batterer takes control over the victim's next breath. It can cause psychological consequences and death. Luckily, Dick left no visible injuries, no scratches, abrasions, or scrapes. She would hide it from everyone. Never to forget. She remained on alert.

She hid her suffering from her colleagues. She asked herself, "How did I survive strangulation?" It was easier to survive before she learned the truth about Dick's attempt to shut down her airway and steal her next breath. She was re-traumatized when she learned Dick applied pressure on her throat, cutting off blood vessels and air flow. There was a difference in the execution. "Oh God, I didn't choke on food," because that's a blockage inside the throat. You choke on food, but they strangle you to death.

Never begging for mercy, terrified and traumatized, Frankie couldn't find her voice or stand up for herself for fear of more brutality. She did not take care of her own needs, instead stared out the window for hours, leaning on her hand, reliving the vicious attack, like a scary movie. Maybe it would have a happy ending next time, she lamented.

The small apartment had a full kitchen, fireplace and sundeck. The center courtyard had been landscaped with palm trees, a working fountain with a koi pond filled with lily pads. It was a mini heaven. This city girl welcomed the soothing sounds of the water and the intermittent splashes of water upon her face. She felt like it was a welcome to paradise. It was already better with this lovely new environment. A new job and lots of new beginnings. Dick must let go of his past, she hoped.

He was always picking fights if anyone peered at her. Incredibly envious of other men, it consumed him. A "fame whore," Dick wanted to be a chick magnet and hang with celebrities. He purchased only designer clothes, expensive cologne and slicked back his hair with Dippity Do. Soon recognizing he had a way of finding women with money, it became his paycheck. Frankie was one of those women, creating a cushy life for him. As he became more indignant and abusive, the more Frankie found herself. She didn't really need him. Currently employed at three jobs, she had a goal. She hoped the "bad boy" had some good in him.

The kitchen would be an utter mess after a long day of working. Dick was out of it, half asleep, half high, with potato chip crumbs on the floor, popcorn thrown across the room and an almost empty cardboard box of his dinner, pizza. Infuriated, Frankie would drop her purse, make a big "Humpf" sound to get Dick's attention. He barely could raise his hand to gesture hello. Mumbling, he would say "I got you dinner," attempting to point his finger in the box's direction of pizza. Frankie got excited for a moment because she loved pizza. However, when she opened the box, there was a single hardened cold slice there for her dinner. She picked it up and flung it into the garbage pail. "Thanks for nothing asshole!" "Huh, honey, I left it for you." Dick's head fell down onto the table, sound asleep. "Wished it fell off," she whispered.

The next evening, Frankie came home from work. All she could think of was sleep. Dick was excited to invite her over to the neighbor's house for a game of Pictionary. "We got new neighbors from Germany." I bet, Frankie thought, tall, slender and blonde too. "C'mon," as he dragged her by the arm out of the door. "I'm tired Dick, I want to rest and eat." "Stop bitching." The elevator door opened, enraged with attitude, he shoved her into the elevator. They made brief introductions. The four of them sat down to get acquainted and play the game. The new hostess was delightful, had a plate of snacks and drinks. At least, thought Frankie, I will have some food.

Dick was acting extra suave, aka cocky, and trying to impress the neighbors. Frankie rolled her eyes and stayed focused on the game. She just wanted this night to be over. Out of the blue, Dick punched her in the shoulder and said, "Play faster." The neighbor stared at him unapprovingly but said nothing. The game was almost over. Dick was boasting how he was winning, laughing obnoxiously, and hitting Frankie on the leg several times. His shift in energy was not good. She thought, "This night cannot go dark. How could it?" Dick pushed his chair quickly away from the table, stood up, and applauded himself for winning. Laughing at them like fools, he went around the table to kiss the lovely woman from Germany. "Hey babe, let's go home."

Once they walked through the door, he shoved Frankie

to the elevator, nearly tripping on her heels. Leaning her
up against the wall, securing her shoulder against the wall,
Frankie became powerless. He attempted to kiss her, but
Frankie briskly turned her head away, causing him to fall
into the wall. Just then, the elevator door opened, and Dick
pushed her, slamming her into the back wall of the elevator.
Frankie shivered inside; her hands were trembling. "Oh shit,"
she murmured, leaning into the forest green wall remaining as
quiet as possible. The cables moved with a little jerk, causing
Frankie to slip and land on her butt. Dick glared at her, doing
nothing to help. Frankie's arm was already sore from the
punches and pulls. She grabbed onto the old brass railing to
pull herself up with dignity.

As they stood in front of the apartment door, she
shook as she put the key in the door lock. Dick pushed it
open abruptly and threw Frankie across the threshold. Again,
tripping over the threshold and the instability of her heels,
she landed face down on the carpet. Frankie struggled for air
and tried to stand up. Dick caught hold of her, flipped her on
her back, and straddled her. Unable to push him off and fight
back, she looked into the eyes of a demon, turned her head as
he denigrated her.

"I made you, you are nothing, nobody from
nowhere!" His hands clutched behind her neck, her body
thrust forward and then went limp. Squeezing tighter, he had
no remorse. He appeared to be somewhere else and had no
fear in attempting murder. Did he pre-meditate all this? Was
he mentally insane, schizophrenic, or bipolar? Frankie didn't

know, she feared for her life as her eyes rolled back into her head. "I'll show you, bitch! I introduce you to people and you embarrass me! You don't like my friends and roll your eyes. I see you judging us, thinking you are better, but remember this, without me you would have nothing!"

He pulled her head, so they were face to face. "Open your eyes!" he demanded. "I made you!" Frankie opened her eyes while he continued to wildly scream at her and spit on her face. He heard himself and saw the terror in Frankie's eyes. Backing off the pressure of his grip, he realized he could return to prison. He fell off to the side and jumped away from Frankie, retreating into a corner, sobbing like a child. He was the one who tried to commit murder and he's sobbing?! Thoughts wandered through her mind.

"You made me do it!" he yelled. "You are just like her, ungrateful." He was groveling as Frankie gave him the finger when he announced, "I love you," and walked away crying. Everyone leaves me, he mumbled.

I made him, do it? Terrified and traumatized, Frankie could not communicate, react or take action for self-preservation or self-dense. How can I make him do something? I don't have that power. Why did I check out and not fight? So many questions ran through her head. Barely able to walk, she found her way to the bed. She survived strangulation twice now. Her brain could not process the aftermath. I will go to sleep, it will go away.

Disgusted, she rolled over and wrapped herself in the leopard blanket for protection. Frankie counted the "I love you's" Dick blabbered as she counted the "Fuck you," she shouted in her head. Stoically, she said "Get the fuck off of me," as she fantasized smashing his skull with the claw end of a hammer. Would she ever have the nerve to do it?

No police needed, there are no marks. My secret is safe, she assured herself.

The sun rose quickly, and Frankie never slept, fearful Dick would kill her for sure. Frankie left for work. His head on the table and a beer bottle in his hand, sound asleep. He never went to bed.

'Never beg for mercy,' the words repeated in her head for weeks. 'Don't give him the satisfaction,' these indignant words played. I wish I understood why I freeze and play dead. My mind goes blank. Where do I hide?

The two of them avoided each other for days. Silence was a learned behavior for Frankie, so it was normal. Dick was always out of it anyway and didn't know what day of week it was, always smoking pot, drinking and falling asleep on the table.

The neighbors didn't seem to care and never spoke a word when Dick's venomous rage appeared. How could they not hear the slamming of her body on the carpet, the screams? Frankie reminisced how growing up in the row homes, people didn't get involved but definitely gossiped. Are they telling stories about me?

Frankie came to understand that Fight was the only option to distract herself from the pain, focus on her escape plan and the crime scene. Fight or Flight - a choice. Dick, the evil doer bastard, she feared would kill her one day and no matter how much he begged for forgiveness and sobbed; she remained focused.

Frankie felt herself crumbling, missing a part of the passion one should have in a relationship. She wanted to be happy. Sleepless nights, long days of work and endless moments of staring out the window, watching the world go by.

Am I being punished for 'using him' to come with me to California? Fearful of living alone, her regret overshadowed her and his bullshit blaming. It was during this realization Frankie vowed to make everyday matter and have no regrets.

*It was time to build her future.*

## Chapter 4
### Too Smart to Be a Secretary

*"Go to hell," Frankie thought. "No one tells me what to do!"*

As graduation day neared, Frankie mapped out her future without Dick. He was desperate, boiling over with rage and jealous of her success. Too dumb to perceive Frankie's rage and disgust, Dick had become nothing and useless to her.

Dick met Portia at the improv classes Frankie paid for. He wanted to be around celebrities and pretty women. However, Frankie had hoped he would use his dramatics and talents to con people as a way of acting to make something of himself. She agreed to pay for the classes and prayed he would become useful and get a job. Portia was an attractive attorney who partnered with her husband, Victor, in their law practice. Her goal was to be an actress one day. Their meeting would be serendipitous. Dick and Portia spent time together on the sundeck rehearsing lines before he introduced Frankie. "What a rude ass he continues to be," her mind chatted. Dick motioned over to Frankie. "I want you to meet Portia. I think you two will have some things in common." Frankie couldn't imagine that at all.

After some small talk about how they met, Portia countered and turned to Frankie and suggested, "I want you to be my secretary." Baffled, Frankie said, "I'm no secretary." Portia countered, "You will be." Perplexed, Frankie did not know what Dick had said to her and why she would offer her this position. Very odd, she thought. "Let's set up a meeting and we can work things out, ok?"

Frankie appreciated the act of kindness and the boost of confidence she wished for. With trepidation but thrilled, she jumped at the second opportunity of her lifetime. "Yes, that would be nice. Thank you."

Now, she could work one job by day and take classes at night. She worked hard on losing her New York accent as well, but she didn't succeed.

Frankie continued plotting how to leave Dick without sharing her secret with anyone, including Portia or Victor, literal legal superheroes, who could have easily planned the escape for her.

Portia, a stunning, blond, hopeful actress and

attorney, had an elegant office with yellow painted walls, floral-patterned curtains, and matching chairs. She listened to classical music while she prepared her legal briefs. She was petite, wore tailored pantsuits, with chunky, but ornate, necklaces. "Thank you very much for this opportunity." "I have a feeling about you. Things are going to go very well for you." Frankie really needed to hear this, but how did she know?

In contrast, Victor's office was masculine, well-appointed with antique furniture and red walls decorated with plaques, photos and newspaper articles about him. Tall and thin, with salt and pepper hair, he wore pinstriped suits, silk ties. He regularly had his wing-tipped shoes shined on the first floor of the building, which Frankie had never seen before.

Things moved quickly and soon she had her own office, piles of cases on her desk. They trained her how to research and prepare for briefs and interviews with the accused. Very excited, she dove in with all her gusto and passion to make something of herself. The whirlwind of kindness, generosity and all the extra hours of work had Frankie on a merry-go-round, one she was enjoying. The two attorneys took a special interest in her career path, even though she didn't understand why. They never judged her, had a warm parental way about them, and sat her down to polish her approach and character.

They wanted her to represent well because they knew she had the spunk to be much more. Frankie went along with it because it felt amazing and to Kat, she was just an uneducated girl, a shop gal. "What was I thinking wanting to be like Kat? Portia is much more my style to emulate." Her office faced the city from the 9th floor. Plopping in her big tan leather chair, she kicked off her shoes and spun around like a carefree kid when no one was looking. Ahh, this was the desire "to be rich and famous."

"Frankie, how would you enjoy attending a fashion show with me?" The words could not pop out of her mouth fast enough. She had never been experienced an event like this. "Absolutely." "Good, let's meet up at my favorite restaurant and then we shall see what's in style for the season. Here is the address," as she handed Frankie a business card from an upscale restaurant.

Frankie had taught herself how to type, finding ways to locate the information she needed to prepare Victor for court, and was honored. She had the initiative and smarts to make them proud of her. This was the contemporary version, educated, successful and professional. No more dancing for a while. However, she was enjoying this unique image, the people were uplifting and admiring her and gaining so much knowledge, like a sponge.

Little did she realize her life was about to be

transformed. They became her initial mentors, offered her opportunities she would never have had, and even took her to the ballet. One afternoon, over reviewing some paperwork, Victor and Portia approached Frankie. Victor spoke first. "We want you to go to law school and become an associate in our criminal defense practice. Someday you may replace Portia when you are ready." Portia added, "You are too smart to be a secretary." Overwhelmed, she soaked it in and thought, "I am smarter than a secretary. I am smart enough to be a lawyer!" Grinning, she looked up at them and nodded and said, "YES!"

Kat had her own idea for Frankie. She invited her to lunch at her favorite Thai Food restaurant. As they walked down the street, Frankie boasted about her plan to enroll in law school. Kat laughed out loud and mocked her, "Don't you have to be smart to be a lawyer?"

Sickened, Frankie glared at the entitled spoiled brat, "I am smart. I ran your stores, and I made you money!" Kat was stunned and at a loss for words, but Frankie couldn't change her mind that day. Despite her lack of support, she was grateful for the business opportunities Kat had offered and she stayed in touch with Kat. Although she informed Kat of her upcoming college graduation, she didn't extend an invitation.

Johnnie would be her first test. Would she be able to handle a homicide?

It was about to get real.

Of all their clients, Johnnie was the most memorable. To prepare for her new career, Victor took her on her first prison tour. It was worse than portrayed on television, with the stench of body odor and graffiti-painted walls. Johnnie's fellow-inmates peeked through the iron bars as they watched Victor and Frankie approach him. She heard her heart beating during the long walk through the smelly hell. Fearing there would be catcalls from the onlookers, she cringed.

Finally, they were escorted by guards to Johnnie's cell. She remained composed on the outside but was a wreck on the inside. She looked up at this 6-foot something blond-haired, blued-eyed murderer. He had tattoos on his neck, arms, face and other places she didn't want to see. Definitely not the kind-hearted client on the other end of the phone, but an actual hard-core criminal. He was wearing the prison-issued orange jumpsuit, with long dirty hair and a smile from ear to ear.

Wearing her only suit and a pearl necklace, in a cell with a murderer, she was taken aback how he presented himself as a gentleman, a Catholic school-boy.

"Hey, Frankie," he stood up and reached towards

her to shake her hand, but they had shackled his hands at his crotch, so she declined the offer.

"Nice to meet you Johnnie," she responded.

Before that jaw-dropping encounter, she didn't judge him, but now she couldn't help herself. His face, neck and arms covered in tattoos; Johnnie was menacing. Frankie spoke with his mother for over two years, until she passed away. Thousands of miles apart from her only son, she never learned the truth about Johnnie.

It was on the beach she ran into Pyper, whom she recognized from home. Often, Frankie took walks to just cry and release her feelings to the ocean. She always enjoyed collecting seashells and making castles when she was a child. Perhaps it was her place of peace and where she felt her best.

Pyper, a counselor, was feisty like Frankie. She would help her process things she didn't understand and enlighten her as they collected shells together. As Pyper walked with her friend Frankie on the beach that summer, with her raspy voice asked, "Wait, that bitch called you dumb?"

This was the pinnacle moment they discussed healing. Now Frankie could heal herself and empower others.

## Chapter 5
### The Gang Murderer

*"Collect call from Johnnie. Will you accept the charges?"*

The son of two homicide detectives, a Catholic school-boy imposter, couldn't be a cold-blooded murderer, could he? In her mind, it wasn't possible. Naïve wanna-be lawyer Frankie was convinced justice would prevail and wrongfully accused, clean-cut altar boy Johnnie, would be freed. She had to be involved somehow in the victory for Johnnie and a chance to work beside Victor.

The prisoners were trapped behind bars, eager to see defenseless prey walk through the halls. Young Frankie, naively dressed to impress Johnnie, in her new role as legal assistant. So different how she dressed as the

Public Defender to shield herself from the perversions and catcalls by the inmates.

Although she had reservations, Frankie desperately wanted to believe in Johnnie's innocence. Maybe her intuition was correct. She had researched the law books to provide support for Victor's closing arguments. She drafted a conclusive brief, the "smoking gun," revealing Johnnie's whereabouts on the night in question. Armed with the law, she implored Victor to include her at Johnnie's trial. She was feeling confident all the bases were covered and Johnnie would be proven innocent.

Based upon her time with him in his cell, the conversations on the phone, and contribution to his defense for the trial, Frankie wrote the best essay on capital punishment. It just happened her Political Science Professor required her to render a decision whether capital punishment was appropriate during the penalty phase of a murder trial. It was a time when strict Catholics believed in an eye-for-an-eye justice system. Not so quick, Portia and Victor held a staunch position against the death penalty.

"What?" "Are these people crazy?" Frankie grew up learning to support the death penalty, because her godfather, a homicide detective, adamantly believed in it.

Confused by these conflicting legal convictions, Frankie had to rely on the evidence and the testimony at Johnnie's trial. She and Victor arrived at the Halls of Justice, awestruck by the shuffling of the prisoners' shackled feet across the asphalt. Each prisoner was accompanied by a Sheriff toting a sidearm and giving the "skunk-eye" to all passing by. Ah yes, this was Frankie's first day of her legal career.

Frankie had chucked her huge earrings and big hair for a suit and pearls, mirroring the attorneys who had paved the way for her. Now she looked like a polished Legal Assistant. Holding her head high, she deliberately approached the massive doors of the Halls of Justice, legal pad in hand.

She had earned the privilege of accompanying Victor, so she didn't flinch at her first pat-down by security. It was the first of many until she was so recognized and respected as a practicing attorney. Frankie's future replaced her past on that day with Victor, the beaten and battered woman, had become fearless. She looked the part and had earned the right to walk among the attorneys, a victor over the batterer. The victim was gone and in her place was the warrior. This secret remained with her for the next thirty years.

Victor escorted her to the courtroom, she searched for the jury box, and arrived at the gallery, taking her place. As she turned to face the bench, where His Honor would preside, a tall, polished man sporting a navy suit smiled at her. "I made it," she thought. "I AM important and whoever that was, noticed it, too." Leaning over to Victor, she whispered, "Who is that?" Victor chuckled and responded, "Johnnie." Victor had paid for a haircut and hand delivered a suit Johnnie's dying mother had sent. It was like the hand of an angel warming the shoulders of her beloved son.

Her jaw dropped, and she remained wide-eyed as she focused on the shackles hidden under Johnnie's navy slacks. She marveled at the metamorphosis from the scraggly haired, nasty smelling gangster to a lawyer looking wrongfully accused. "Nice job, Victor," she added.

It was finally Johnnie's turn to testify, although he should have kept his big mouth shut and accepted a deal. Instead, he turned to Frankie, smiled and readily took the stand for direct examination by Victor, followed by a merciless cross-examination by the prosecution. Johnnie testified he was on the east coast the day of the murder and there was no way he could have been at the scene of the crime. "Genius," thought Frankie. After all, she was the one who had prepared the legal brief, proving he was in Maine on the day and time of the murder. "We got this," she concluded, and of course, so did Johnnie.

"They had it coming," he testified. "It was a drug deal gone bad, really bad. We ambushed them outside the bar, and they didn't even see it coming!" Frankie had sloppily written his chilling account on her legal paid during one interview. She shuddered as she recalled the macabre description of how they had shot the victims in the back and stashed them in a nearby dumpster.

Johnnie continued his testimony, voice getting more excited. "It was a gang related hit!" The offspring of two homicide detectives to whom the dead didn't matter, was unapologetic. The brutal cross-examination gave Johnnie the stage. What we fear, he relished. His true heinous colors were revealed as he methodically described the bloody murder and pre-planned disposal of two human beings, two fellow-gang members.

During his testimony, Frankie noticed his cocky grin accompanied by the tattoos on his face, one that proudly identified him as a gang member, and two teardrops identifying him as a murderer.

Frankie was stunned. "Holy Shit," he really was in fact a killer and she had been coddling him for two years by phone. He may have deceived her, but he would not fool the jury. After witnessing his deplorable testimony, Frankie felt her stomach go into knots, partly because of the gory details and partly because Johnnie was facing the death penalty. She felt nauseated after staring into the eyes of a killer. As he shuffled back to the holding cell, feet still shackled, Frankie refused to look at Johnnie. She even refused to be present for the verdict and sentencing.

The jury found him guilty of two counts of murder in the first degree, Now, Victor had to fight for "life without parole" (LWOP) and against the death penalty without Frankie at his side. He understood her position as the testimony and the photographs of the dead had overwhelmed her. She was equipped with enough information for her to complete her essay, and published her position, an "eye for an eye," supporting the death penalty.

Johnnie avoided the death penalty because of Victor's "mad skills" and sentenced to serve LWOP. He would ultimately die in a dark cell, with the stench of lies and prisoners consuming him.

With Johnnie's testimony still ringing in her ears to this day, Frankie counsels her clients to, "Live your life like you are on the witness stand." She prepared for her legal career, aspiring to be like one of the stylish sharks on "LA Law." As college graduation approached, she searched for local law schools. Portia and Victor attended her graduation, cheering loudly as she crossed the stage for her diploma. Her family had sent her roses along with a congratulatory note.

The evening before graduation, Kat sheepishly called Frankie, inviting her to a celebratory dinner. They met at Frankie's favorite Italian restaurant, just blocks away from the office. Arriving at the table, Kat grabbed Frankie, hugged her before taking their seats. Popping the cork, they toasted to Frankie's future and liberation from Dick.

As they sat waiting for their Fettucine Alfredo, Kat became teary-eyed. "I was wrong," she sobbed. "You have everything, and I have nothing. Robbie left me for a younger woman, after all these years." Tears falling down her face, she revealed her son was still addicted to drugs, and her affluent millionaire father remained cold and loveless. "You have a family and parents who love you! You earned this success on your own! You definitely have a future." Frankie had proven her wrong. "I am NOT too dumb to be a lawyer!" she smiled inwardly.

Following the commencement ceremony, Portia and Victor treated her to a lavish outdoor brunch, toasting her achievements with Mimosas. They presented her with their gift, the Law School Admission Test preparation course, wrapped with a bow, so she could test in San Francisco and immediately apply to law school. Frankie was speechless, thrilled, and felt spoiled for the first time in her life.

"Thank you for all you have done for me".

### Chapter 6
### The Earth Shook

*My life would change in 15 seconds*

A massive earthquake far away is like a gentle bump followed several moments later by stronger rolling and shaking that may seem like sharp shaking for a short while.

Streets collapsing, gas lines burst, flames, fumes. The rocking of the earth was violent, and it will be challenging to stand up. There was a thin column of smoke, ascending gradually up into the sky. We struggled to rescue people, but the intensity of the flames pushed us backward. No one can comprehend the catastrophe to San Francisco in its entirety. I was one of the fortunate ones, for neither personal injury nor death visited my household. We braced ourselves in the doorway, clinging to the casing, wondering if we would survive.

It was a sweltering hot day in October in 1989. The city was eerily quiet, as if something was going to happen. It didn't feel good.

Victor, always diligent and prepared, handed Frankie a package to hand deliver before the day was over. She hurried to the tall glass building, delivered the package and rushed back to the office. It was too quiet. Something didn't feel right at all. The sky had a mystical color of magenta and oranges blending as the day would soon come to an end.
Hurrying to the elevator to get to her desk, she thought she heard a rumble. It wasn't unusual to feel trembling living in California. This time it grew steadily stronger. The building shook sideways. Frankie's body rocked back and forth, unable to get a steady stance. The desks were rattling and moving across the carpet when Victor screamed, "Frankie, get in the doorway!" She followed orders, feeling unnerved while everything happened so quickly. "And stay away from any glass and take cover!"

Frankie felt tremors before, but there was never any visible damage. They stood in the door jamb and held onto the door frame, while the building shook from left to right. "When will it be over?" she thought. When the shaking stopped, they saw smoke and dust in the hallway before the lights went out.

The secretary down the hall stood in her doorway, pleading for help. No one could reach her. Debris had fallen from above and the floor outside of her door had fallen through, so it trapped her behind a gaping hole. Hopefully, emergency responders could rescue her.

Just then, Victor realized Portia had gone out for coffee, blocks away, and never returned. Panicked, he guided Frankie, who was shaking, down nine flights of stairs, in the dark, inhaling dust and climbing over debris. They collided with Portia, running up the stairs, with coffee in her hands, to check on Frankie and Victor. She fell into Victor's secure arms, careful not spill his coffee and the two quickly gave thanks and escaped out of the building.

The three escaped the smoke and debris, hyperventilating they wandered outside. Squinting, rubbing their eyes, pasty white skin like a vampires fearful of the sun, they went into the light. Brushing off the drywall plaster from their clothes and hair, they regained a sense of gravity. It was a miracle they were alive.

They stood there stunned, streets lifted and cracked, glass blown from windows, cars overturned and people scurrying to get help. We had no cell phones back then and had to come up with a plan quickly.

Willing hands were lifting and turning the great stones out of the streets, and finally the frightened police horses hauled out debris that, in ordinary times, would have been insurmountable.

The breeze had shifted, showering us with ashes and stinging our eyes with smoke from the constant increasing fire. In shock themselves, Portia and Victor felt they had to create a plan for Frankie. While strategizing for the three of them, they zig-zagged through the fallen brick, the unidentifiable rubble, and the shards of glass sprinkled in the mix.

"Frankie, we don't know if there will be aftershocks, so we have to push through it and get to the other side. What is your plan?" Victor inquired.

All she could say, blankly, staring into his eyes and with a heavy heart, Frankie mumbled, "I hope it buried him under the rubble."

"Snap out of it!" Portia demanded. "How will you find Dick?" Victor asked. No response from Frankie. Quite unusual for a gal who always seemed in control. She was too shocked to say anything.

"Wait here, let me get the car." Before Portia could beg him to stay, he was gone in a flash. The two women held each other as every bone in their body shivered. Frankie couldn't think straight, and she had no plan but did realize this earthquake was a symbol of her life.

Victor appeared out of nowhere from the underground garage with his BMW. How he got through all the wreckage was beyond comprehension and no one asked. "Jump in." They dodged other escape cars, navigating the hazardous roads, tragedy and trauma around them. An overturned bus, a gridlock of cars stopped them in their tracks, their minds unable to comprehend the devastation. While speeding through red lights and stop signs, they surveyed the never-ending apocalyptic scene. Dodging falling bricks, they ran over unidentifiable bumps in the road and soaked in the horror show.

Victor clicked on the car radio to hear instructions from the emergency service agency. Just then, they heard a report. A woman had been decapitated on the path Frankie had traveled that morning. It was outside the glass skyscraper, where Frankie delivered Victor's urgent documents. Stunned, Frankie realized if she had walked any slower or left the building any later, she could have been fatally injured.

How many times will I face death, thought invincible Frankie? Now in the back seat of the BMW with two protectors, she realized she wasn't invincible; she must protect herself and she MUST heed the warnings. With life so fragile, and danger so unpredictable, she had to break the cycle. Angels were watching over her.

What would Frankie find at the penthouse? The sky grew purple as the sun descended upon the city with a luminescent glow over the debris. She jumped out of the car quickly, thanking her friends, and scurried to her apartment. The streets were torn up so bad, she could barely walk in her heels. Dammit, she threw off her shoes and ran home, being cautious she didn't step on broken glass.

Neighbors were panicked, running up and down the stairs, kids crying. Frankie became unnerved. She could no longer stand the anticipation of what she was about to confront. She was scared for the first time. Would she find Dick dead? After all, she wanted him gone. Surely, she didn't have the power to create an earthquake to get rid of him? Drug dealer Clay waved to her as strangers wandered in a zombielike state. You think the jerk would offer to help people. Focus, Frankie said to herself, as she ran up four flights of stairs, a mother crying for help, people trapped and others providing instructions and encouragement help was on the way. Surely, they would be rescued, wouldn't they? she thought.

She shoved the door open. Empty. Where was Dick, she panicked. Under a collapsed bookcase? The goddamn phones were dead and there was no way to reach out for help or call her family. It would soon be dark and with no electricity, what would she do? Ice was already melting from the refrigerator and the cabinets swung open, dishes broken and cornflakes on the floor. "I wonder if he is buried somewhere gasping for breath," she hoped.

Clueless that aftershocks happened, she ran back down four flights, sat on the steps and helplessly waited for Dick. Why did she even care? She had no plan of escaping the chaos and no plan of escaping him.

It grew steadily worse, the noise deafening; the crash of dishes, falling pictures, the rattle of the flat metal roof, bookcases being overturned, the piano hurled across the parlor, the grumble and straining of the building itself, shattered glass and falling plaster, made such a roar, no one noise could be distinguished. Echoing sounds of crying filled the air.

Parts of the city were on fire and the neighbors could see it from the rooftop in the black of night. Without electricity, they all emptied the freezers, fired up the charcoal and cooked all that was salvageable. "Burgers for everyone on the roof," they offered to neighbors and people they never knew, including the weirdo next door who they assumed was a fugitive.

The hospital, a low stone structure with a tiled roof was destroyed. The stone front had virtually all fallen away, the chimney gone, and everything twisted. The timber supporting the roof was exposed and the stone arch entrance crumbled before their eyes. The attendants were frantically making efforts to get the ambulance out to help those in need. Stones were wedged everywhere, piles of them, and the door to the ambulance was so wedged it would not open. Everyone felt helpless.

After hours of nervously waiting, Dick ran towards her, up the steps, two at a time. He boasted, "I grabbed a friend, and we searched for you at the office and then at school." He sobbed and grabbed her to assure her she was safe now that he found her. "Really asshole, how many times do I have to survive before you get lost," thought Frankie. She was hoping she would never see him again.

The earth stood still as they sheltered in place. With no hot water, she showered in the freezing cold water. It didn't matter. School was closed, the office was closed, and they waited for word whether the building would be demolished. They were both alive, but Frankie was nearly dead inside.

Remnants of memories would remain in her heart. No longer would she sit in Kat's magnificent suite or tour the city. The Wharf chocolate factory with its mounds of truffles, ice cream, candy swirl pops... gone. No more cable car rides or stops at Fisherman's Wharf, the aroma of salt water, fish and chips and trips to the candy shop. Destroyed, in a blink of an eye.

Frankie realized her relationship was like the earthquake. The tremors shook her senses, the fractures of the foundation built upon a broken core, their love story. It was never sustainable.

Now, stuck with Dick, she was "calling all angels" to pull her from his path of destruction.

Frankie's world was rocked by abuse, and when it finally ended, she had to build and repair herself. No hugs, no judges, no police, no therapy.

*It took thirty years before she knew why...*

## Chapter 7
Hide the Hammer

*The plan was in place*

The days dragged on, and every night Frankie tossed and turned while he laid beside her sleeping peacefully. Her troubles consumed her. She had to pay the bills, while he purchased weed with the money she allotted him. Tuition was a priority to become a lawyer. Kicking the sheets off her leg, it was virtually impossible to get comfortable with so many concerns swirling around her head. The alarm clock ticking grew louder every second she lost sleep. I have to keep my grades up and perform effectively at work. I need to sleep; she told herself.

Tonight, she agonized over the last assault, while Dick was evidently dreaming of rolling a joint, taking a deep inhale and chasing it with candy as he imagined hanging out with rock stars.

She didn't deserve this life and recognized it. "I'm better than this," she rationalized. "He's the bad boy, I'm the good girl." Evaluating her choices and decisions, she recognized she should have left him behind. Now, she was paying for manipulating him to protect her. Repeating in her head, she would hear, "Don't give up. Stick to the plan. Hit me, you prick, and you are dead."

Each day, the anxiety built as drug dealers entered the penthouse. Money stolen, and she learned Dick was cheating on her. There were way too many close calls. With her hand over her mouth, gnawing on her fingers, she uttered "Get the fuck out," repeatedly. Dick knew she disapproved of his lifestyle and could care less. He was a slob, contemptuous, arrogant, and a schemer.

The landlord noticed Frankie walking home from work. "May I speak with you for a moment?" Frankie nodded. "You do realize there are dope dealers at your apartment, including the Notorious Clay?" Humiliated and fuming, she rushed to the apartment only to find it empty. Moments afterward, Dick strolled in all happy-go-lucky. Enraged, she blasted him, "Are you out of your mind?" Dealer Clay stepped in next, without even knocking, wearing his felt fedora. "Yo Frankie." "Screw you Clay, get the hell out. You practically got me evicted from MY apartment!" she shouted. Dick just chomped on his potato chips, sipping a can of open soda.

"Frankie, mind your own business and get the hell out of here. You don't like my friends or me, so what the hell are you doing here?"

This could be the moment. Her heart was pounding. Breathe, brace yourself. Clay left quietly, and Dick shut the door. He walked towards Frankie, high as a kite, and gloated about the girl he met last night and how much weed he scored. This dude is a lunatic, she thought. Does he not notice what is happening under his nose? Or am I the one so blind?

"I'm going home! I am attending law school and you are not coming." Infuriated, he roared, "You're not flying home! You're not going to law school, and you are not leaving me! NO one leaves me!" As his eyes got redder and his face angrier, Frankie thought, this is it, he's going to strike me.

Looking towards the kitchen sink, she backed away gradually. Her notebooks were on the table. She braced herself while picking them up. Here it comes, close your eyes, don't grab the hammer, let him touch you and stick to the plan!

Dick charged towards her, hollering, "You're not moving anywhere!" He wound up his right arm like a pitcher ready to pitch a ball. With all his might, closing his fist, he cold-cocked Frankie on the left side of her head. Stunned and in excruciating discomfort, her face swelling. "You are fucking done!" He knew it. She had control now, Dick realized.

Frankie was quivering, hysterical, and felt a sharp throbbing in her neck and head. Grabbing the phone, she called her parents. She would require a witness if she took him to court. "I'm coming home," she cried into the phone.

"He hit me!" Everything was a blur. Things happened rapidly, emotions soaring and Dick standing there like a nitwit, frightened of his own tail. In her frantic state, she could not even recall what her mother replied and ended the call. "Get the hell out!" Dick had no escape plan, and he needed a get out of jail card before she slammed his ass in one. Frankie knew she required medical attention. I have to pass this freaking history exam. I have no time for doctors.

It was a long night and both Frankie and Dick sobbed, although she did not know what his tears were about. She doubted he had remorse. Trembling and deaf in one ear, she walked to the university and sat down for the grueling exam. Her professor peered at her, attempting to assess her circumstances, but too indifferent to figure out why she was sniffling and trembling. No one cares, she reflected, no one wants to listen.

Portia and Victor surely could be her legal superheroes, but Frankie never shared her secret and Dick would never confess.

Exhausted from hours of the grueling exam with no sleep, Dick groveling for her to stay with him, her trauma consumed her. Now she needed to call the law clerk's office and tell Ann she was sick.

"I can't understand you Frankie, speak up and stop crying." "Sure Ann, I'll stop crying on demand after being beaten and losing my hearing." "What?!" Damn, Frankie slammed the payphone and shut her mouth. Now to trudge her way to the emergency room and get some help.

It was a long mile to City Hospital and overwhelmed by fear and a potential brain injury; not knowing what she would face at the hospital. She dreaded the truth but refused to share her secret with anybody, not even the police or hospital. She was ashamed.

Dick made absolutely no attempt that morning to comfort Frankie or accompany her to the emergency room. It was outside his comfort zone. Instead, he had the audacity to appear at the emergency room high on weed with his next victim. A young babe on his arm in tight clothing and ready for anything.

"Hey babe." Fuming, Frankie summoned the hospital security guard to escort them both away, like criminals. The guard didn't even pick up on anything, ask questions, and ignored the signs of possible abuse. He kept the peace at the hospital.

Frankie's secret included lying for Dick as well. She said a basketball hit her head during a ball game. It was an accident and no one's fault. The attending physician was extremely tired or lazy to give a damn about the truth or the safety of Frankie.

Three hours drifted by in the ER with a diagnosis of a perforated eardrum. She prayed it would not be permanent and was referred to a specialist. How would I pay for it she wondered? If the hole didn't heal, she would face a skin graft, they said. Some part of her body would be harvested to patch the hole in the eardrum. WTF, how could this happen to me? I just don't get it.

It would be an arduous walk home by herself, with the annoying sound of the ocean rumbling in her left ear. Please, dear God, restore my hearing. I don't deserve this. Block after block, she hollered, "I hate him. I hate him. I should've used the hammer. I hate him."

When she arrived at the penthouse, Dick was chomping on candy with his customary high on weed. He needed it to calm his nerves. "You are going to pay for these medical bills!" The weak prick laughed and declared, "Really? I doubt it bitch." He would not even chip in, though this was his crime. Frankie pulled out her health insurance card and began calling to make an appointment with the specialist. She hoped it would shame him into giving a shit. How does a self-centered manipulator give a shit? They don't, she realized.

Nervously, she dialed the phone, focusing on her plan to get rid of Dick once and for all, when she slammed the phone down in anger. "Pack up your shit and get out!" He just stared at her, giggling from his high. Controlling her temper so she didn't grab the hammer and wind up in jail, she continued, "Don't steal anything on the way out!" Dick just ignored her.

"Damn him, I have to get out of here before I do something I regret!" Frankie went into her room to pack a small bag, her jewelry, and checkbook. She made a call to the airline for tickets back home. Her college discount helped with the price, providing some relief. They exchanged no words for the rest of the evening. The only sound was the one annoying Frankie in her ear.

As usual, Dick left for the evening, presumably somewhere with his new chick. At least Frankie could get some rest without worrying about another altercation.

A tremendous bang woke Frankie around 6 a.m. "What the?" She hopped out of bed, thinking it was an earthquake. Turned out it was the slimy creep who tried to kill her three times, stumbling over himself after a long drug and sex induced evening, she guessed. "Get out NOW and never come back!"

"Give me the money for rent and I will go." With a swift turn to her purse, Frankie pulled out $750.00 and her Christmas bonus. It was a small price for freedom, she figured. Throwing the money at his chest, he snorted. "I mean it Dick, get the hell out of my life!" He wobbled over to the couch with the money clenched in his hand and fell off into a deep sleep instantly.

Ok, I got this, she thought, clutching her purse and luggage. The flight home would be stressful with her ear. Hopefully, her family would open their arms to her and provide support. It was a dream she hoped and prayed for many days.

The taxi was waiting downstairs, and Frankie was daydreaming of her new way of life and career. Once in her seat on the airplane, she opened up one magazine from the chair's back pocket. Stretching out her legs, she flipped through the pages. A deluxe hotel beamed across the glossy page, more charming than anything she had ever known. Each page adorned with beautiful places to visit, luxurious restaurants and fancy jewelry putting a smile on her face "I could live this life."

"Would you like something to drink?" the flight hostess asked. Still shaking a bit from everything that occurred over the last few days, Frankie needed a drink. "A merlot, please."

A movie sounded good to pass the time away. Clicking through the choices she came upon, "The Outsiders," displaying top handsome male stars on the icon. She couldn't resist. The opening scene was a young adolescent male daydreaming in school. He opened his composition book and wrote *"When I stepped out"*... writing about his dreams, Frankie related. The background melody had her fantasizing as she sipped her wine. She closed her eyes and heard the words *loved* and *cared for*... yes, that was her desire. Relaxing in her seat, they dimmed the lights for the red eye flight. All the words to the song reminded her of her life. Filled with sorrow and compassion, salty tears rolled down the side of her eyes. Just then she heard, "How you doin'?" when three punk boys appeared on the screen, tough and trouble written all over them. This is too close to home, she realized. Slicked back hair, black shiny pointed boots and attitude, lots of it. As they turned the corner, three young boys were hanging out and playing cards in the grass.

The main character, the bad guy, bullied the boys, grabbed their cards and teased them. "Like to play 52 pick up?" he laughed, throwing the cards up into the air. Frankie spaced, thinking about the days she protected the little kids from being bullied. A nauseous feeling overcame her.

"Excuse me," she motions to the stewardess. "Yes ma'am, may I help you?"

"Can I get some crackers or cookies? I have had nothing to eat all day?" "Would you like a sandwich?" "That would be amazing, yes, please." "Shut your trap!" Frankie jumped as the main character, who reminded her of Slick, yelled at a dark-haired chick in the scene. She had a similar attitude to Frankie. "Leave us alone. Get lost Loser!" "I know when I'm not wanted," he yells.

She clicked off the movie and wanted no more signs and memories. The kind stewardess served her the sandwich and poured another glass of wine. Exhausted from all the trauma and pain in her ear, she closed her eyes after finishing the last sip of wine, which helped ease the pain.

"We are approaching the airport and landing in 45 minutes." She jumped up, slightly confused where she was. "Coffee, I need coffee." Magically, the stewardess was already pouring her a cup and offering her breakfast. I can get used to this lifestyle, she smiled to herself.

I can do this, she whispered to herself. I'm going to have a wonderful Christmas and have fun shopping and celebrating the festivities with my family. Then I can start my new life without Dick.

When she arrived in New York, snowflakes were sprinkling on the trees, the sun glittering through every flake and bringing a joyful energy to Frankie's wounded heart.

"Hey Frankie," she heard old neighbors and friends shouting from the windows. "Nice to have you home for the holidays."

Frankie waved and smiled as she approached the steps to her parents' home. She was hesitant and concerned about how they may react after her last phone call. The door swung open and was greeted by her sisters and mom. I'm safe again. "Come, Frankie, eat. You must be starving. I made your favorite, meatballs." One thing you can count on in life was knowing mom's feeding you her love. It felt good to be home, and she did not have to look over her shoulder, worrying if a punch or choke-hold was coming as a surprise. Dad stood there quietly as Frankie approached him for a brief hug. "Hi Dad."

"Sit, sit, Mangia." Mom had decorated the table with fake poinsettia flowers, golden Christmas balls, and plastic garland. The Christmas tree lights were blinking rainbow colors with a few small packages placed under the tree.

"It's good to be home. Thank you, everyone, for welcoming me back." "Eat, Frankie. I cooked all night. Mangia!" No one wanted to speak about anything, especially the abuse. So, we ate. Frankie stuffed down Christmas cookies Grandma made while they stuffed away my near-death experience.

The next day, Frankie enjoyed Christmas shopping with her thirteen credit cards. She wanted to surprise everyone with something special and find herself some classy outfits for her new venture in law school. Her jaw and ear were in pain, but she kept moving in Frankie Fashion. Nothing was going to stop her.

Christmas carols played in all the stores, elegantly adorned with garland and red bows. Santa was ringing his bell, and the clerks dressed like Santa's helpers. Packages were being wrapped in shiny paper with big, enormous bows. They caught Frankie's eye. "Oh, I must get these wrapped for my sisters. They will love it." It was the first time she was happy and hopeful in years.

Over the next few days, she would assist Grandma in the kitchen, dance to some Christmas tunes and watch Court TV every day to prepare for law school. It was a merry time celebrating with the family.

"Grandma, mom, you out did yourselves with the meatballs, bragoli and pastries. OMG I'm in heaven!" she exclaimed joyfully. Frankie enjoyed every morsel of homemade delicacies, including the crusty Italian bread, even though she had sharp pain in her jaw from the blow to her head. An extra care package with Christmas cookies went home with her to California. A refreshed feeling, hopeful and ready for her entrance exam for law school.

Free of Dick, she boarded the plane, ready to enjoy a quiet evening in her apartment, a good night's sleep finally. Frankie hadn't been this happy in a very long time. Running up the stairs like a little girl, she opened the door to her home.

"Goddammmit Dick!" Oblivious as usual, he waved two golden tickets in front of her face. "We're going to the New Year's Eve Gala." "Shit. You used my paycheck for these tickets, didn't you? This is it!" she shouted. "The last straw! I will go to the Gala and then GET out! Got it?" He nodded yes.

Did he really believe he could win her back? Frankie grew to hate him more every day leading up to New Year's Eve. The only good thing, he spent most nights out and she didn't have to sleep with him. "It's almost over," Frankie told herself while standing on her balcony looking into the starry night sky. These attacks played in her head repeatedly. It was too stressful each day. She would walk past the spot where she left her body, unable to comprehend what happened, but realizing there is a reason she was still alive. Flashbacks and nightmares were frequent. Her goal was to stay strong and away from the hammer and become a successful attorney.

She got through a long night of dancing in her tight suede pumps with the idiot pothead. The walk home from the Gala was tormenting. It's time to fix the broken pieces my way, she kept reminding herself.

*At least she hid the hammer and no one else got hurt.*

## Chapter 8
### The Flight Home

*Frankie didn't choose to fit in, she preferred to stand out*

Frankie accepted the offer to practice law with Portia and Victor as a criminal defense attorney. The second opportunity of her life, she had reached it with serious work and conviction. With a lengthy road ahead of her, Frankie acknowledged the reality she couldn't survive in San Francisco. There was rent to be paid and tuition for law school. She realized many things and life would transform.

The number of hurdles she would encounter would be arduous, including the two-day Bar Exam. Her strategy, rational or not, was to achieve Doctor of Jurisprudence. If Victor and Portia believed and trusted in her with their law practice, it was time she understood the same within herself. Armed with a Bachelor of Arts Degree in Business Administration (B.A.), and "mad secretarial skills," they accepted her into law school, one hour one-way from home. Self-confident, she was ready to face the challenge of four years of night classes on Mondays, Wednesdays and Saturday mornings.

She bought bridal magazines and scanned the pages for her fairy tale wedding gown. Although Slick's cheating and Dick's beating jaded her, she felt deeply she deserved her fairytale dream life. It would pass the time away on her flight back East. Who knows, she giggled, maybe my prince will come.

The countdown began when Frankie booked her flight on the "red-eye" home. She displayed her B.A. and her Delta ticket on the refrigerator, both representing her tickets for her destiny. She made it, she earned it, she wasn't looking back, she craved it all.

The polished, modern, black kitchen set, the bedroom set and the futon near the fireplace had to go, along with the painful reminders. Dave, the next door neighbor, had heard Dick cold-cock her but did nothing to help, purchased the bedroom set. As he hauled furniture, he revealed how worried he was but didn't want to get entangled.

"Are you alright?" he asked. "Enjoy the furniture!" Thank God he didn't call the police, what a shitty neighbor, but grateful he kept her secret.

Next, she returned Dick's rented VHS tape player and television to the electronics store, where he got his weed.

One more reminder of Dick, gone. A few of her classmates turned out to pick up the futon, the toaster oven, and the kitchen items. After word-of-mouth advertising through acquaintances, she donated the remaining furnishings to charity.

With the apartment empty of furniture and nightmares, she wandered towards the kitchen sink, the location of the final brutal assault. She slowly knelt down and opened the cabinet door. After closing her eyes, taking a deep breath, she reached under the pipes and pulled out the hammer to hold in both hands. *I made it. I didn't kill him.*

No tears now. Memories of crying at night, scheming how to lodge the claw-side into the back of his head, vanished. Relieved of the plan of escape she contrived with a splash of rage and a dash of fear was a triumph. She returned the hammer to its home under the sink to be used for the appropriate uses. *Thank goodness no one saw this or knew what I was thinking.*

Finally, Frankie chucked her disco wardrobe, even her purple leather jacket and leggings down the trash chute and into the dumpster. Never to be worn by anyone again. During her last year in San Francisco, she assembled professional attire, via the sale rack at Macy's, for her makeover from retail manager to legal professional. She rewarded herself each time with a chocolate truffle from the candy store.
Smugly, she walked one mile home, showing off her huge red Macys shopping bag. She packed three satiny blouses, two pairs of black trousers, one navy suit and one college sweatsuit in her no longer acceptable oversized suitcase.

Long gone were Frankie's obnoxious earrings and her big hair. She had a more subdued style slicked back in a long, sleek ponytail. With her red nail polish in the trash, Frankie was ready for a French manicure to complement her perpetual California tan.

The night before her departure, she set out her black dress, leopard flats, and pearl earrings. To top it off, she added Dick's designer tortoise shell sunglasses and chunky suede heels, so she looked the part of a jet-setter. She went up got into her bed one last time, before a classmate picked it up for his apartment. A deep sigh of reprieve, she closed her eyes, thanked God she was alive... and so was Dick.

Comfy and snug under the blankets, with a fire roaring in the fireplace. Her memories of Dick's ruthless attacks replaced with delightful dreams and visions of a spectacular life. Finally, purely "good trouble" would consume her.

Morning came quick. Frankie picked up her suitcase and pleasantly took her last jaunt down four flights. On the way out, she stopped, placed her suitcase down, and dug into her purse for a lucky coin. Making a wish, she flipped it into the koi pond. She gazed at the fountain, welcomed the last splashes on her face, and relinquished her past.

No farewell celebration, just a hug from Lina, the landlord, when she turned over her key to the penthouse. It didn't matter to Frankie, because her accomplishments and aspirations were sufficient. Besides, weeks before, she celebrated with Portia and Victor over Mimosas, and toasted to her victory with Kat.

After departing the shuttle and arriving at the airport check-in, a dark, handsome and welcoming check-in officer greeted her. Grinning from ear to ear, and thinking, "Is he flirting with me?" she gave him her ticket and started small talk about her journey home. His name was Mark. He wished her well and directed her to the appropriate waiting section. He explained, "Frankie, I will call you over when it is time to board the airplane."

Although Frankie had flown coast to coast every Christmas and summer, she was never met with such attention. Finally, she received the special treatment she desired. Ready to board the "red-eye," still beaming, Mark waved her over to board the plane, directed her to the proper flight attendant, and then waved goodbye. He was definitely noticing the new Frankie, and she enjoyed it.

Frankie, with her California tan and slicked back hair, confidently boarded the flight to her future. "No one needs to know I am carrying a faux designer carry-on bag," she surmised. She handed the flight attendant her college-discounted ticket, escorted to her seat in the first row of first class. With excitement, she adhered to the instructions and assumed her position in the comfy white leather seat.

Before she could express anything, her shrimp cocktail and white wine appeared, just as illustrated in her Travel & Leisure Magazine. She lowered her tray and reflected, "I learned etiquette and grace from Kat, Portia, and Victor. I am ready for this." With her heart pounding, she glimpsed at the well-dressed business executive seated next to her and confessed, "This is my first time in first class." He replied, "I'm Steve, please take the window seat and enjoy the ride into the clouds."

Self-Assured Frankie sipped her drink and enjoyed the shrimp while gazing into the clouds. She literally was "on Cloud 9." That handsome devil at the airport gifted her with an upgraded ticket and the assurance that she, too, was first class. Unable to relax, Frankie enjoyed every minute of first class, including the filet mignon dinner and apple pie à la mode for dessert.

There was a little turbulence, a few moans from frightened passengers, and all was back to smooth sailing. The first class flight attendant stopped by each passenger to make sure everything was good.

"Do you want anything else, Madame, before the lights go out?" She nodded her head no thanks and turned on her Walkman.

Now, what else might occur on this journey of transformation? she wondered and inserted her favorite CD. While enjoying the tunes of "You Gotta have Faith" by George Michael, Frankie wore a big grin. She glanced up for a moment to notice a handsome couple walking towards the restroom, holding hands. At first, she thought how sweet and then she thought "it can't be," giggling.

They wore matching leather jackets and Jordache jeans. Once the coast seemed clear, they slipped into the tiny restroom and the red 'occupied' light blinked on. Wow, there really is a Mile High Club! Frankie had only heard people whisper about it. It's not a rumor, Frankie witnessed it. Well, she saw the couple go into the restroom, and wondered, did anyone else notice? Her curious mind wandered. How did they get their pants off without stumbling? She really wanted to ask someone if they had ever tried it, but that's not classy. Mostly, she wanted to see how the woman was standing on those high-heeled sandals.

Doesn't anyone else hear them moaning? Surely, the flight attendant is aware? Thirty minutes went by, and the light went green. The devious couple calmly escaped and strolled down the aisle while most people had their eyes closed. Hmm, I wonder if they are honeymooners? I hope they washed their hands. The chatter in her head got noisier. Who cares? I'm seated in first class, a sign of events to come, and I will cherish these memories.

While most people were resting or sleeping, the movie was ready to come up. She wrapped the blanket around her shoulders and the screen popped open. "Pretty Woman," the perfect story for this journey home. "Some dreams come true, some don't, but keep on dreamin'." Truer words never spoken. Just like the character, Edward Lewis, who conquered his fear of heights, Frankie was just about to conquer hers, fearlessly.

Just before dosing off, Frankie recalled the advice of Portia and Victor. "Once you become an attorney, your family will treat you differently and many will resent you." That will never happen, she told herself. "We will hold your job for you," they promised. "Will someone serve us donuts in the morning like Bennie on LA Law?" she hoped. "I love a glazed donut!" Everyone giggled.

A law student now, Frankie was grateful for all her lessons and transformation into a newer version of herself. Her secret from abuse will remain for 30 years. Dozing off to sleep, Frankie dreamed.

The captain made an announcement, jolting Frankie out of her deep sleep along with the smell of freshly brewed coffee being served.

"Good morning, would you like a hot towel and some coffee?" "Yes, thank you." I can get used to this. Except climbing over this guy to get to the bathroom is not my idea of luxury. The turbulence made Frankie lose her balance and almost fall into the lap of the gentleman in the next seat, a hot, gorgeous Adonis.

"Whoops, my apologies." He gently caught her from landing across his body. They both smiled and said good morning. Grinning from ear to ear, Frankie attempted to freshen up in the bathroom. Hmm, smiling as she brushed her teeth. "I wonder what it would be like with that hottie in this tiny space with me. Never going to happen, I'm a good girl."

As she made her way back to her seat, the savvy flight attendant announced they would be starting their breakfast service. Fresh omelet, bacon and biscuits, a side of fruit and another hot cup of deliciously brewed origin coffee. The chef made everything fresh, she said. "Was she serious? Doesn't really matter. One day I will have my own personal chef and he will be tall, strong and cook for me and feed me." A girl could dream.

The captain announced they would be landing in twenty minutes and to prepare for arrival. A rush of panic ran through Frankie with a deep sigh. "Everything will be fine. They will welcome me home and I will graduate with my law degree. Life is good."

Everyone stood quickly to grab their luggage from the overhead compartment and rush home to loved ones or jobs. It was different for Frankie now. Carefully exiting the plane, she took her time walking down the steps onto the runway. Graceful, Frankie. Walk in grace, she repeated in her head. Fantasizing, she imagined waving like a queen to the people ready to greet her. Would anyone recognize her?
The airport was quiet. Her eyes wandered around to see a familiar face. No one.

A man was holding a sign with her name. "Are you Frankie, ma'am?" "Yes." "A friend sent me to take you home."

Interesting, she thought, curious who the mystery person might be and was sad no one showed up for her. Well, it is really early in the morning, and this is surely a first class way to arrive home.
*I shall get used to this lifestyle.*

*Frankie, Esquire*

*Chapter 9*
Doctor of Jurisprudence

*Drop your pencils, hands off your book*

She traveled the long winding road from legal secretary to law student, and none of it was in her plan. The law chose Frankie, and she knew she had more transforming to do to become respected, credible and an advocate for those who could not speak for themselves.

During her first year of law school, Supreme Court Justice Sandra Day O'Connor affirmed Roe vs. Wade, and a woman's right to choose. Now back on the East Coast, she faced backlash from classmates and relatives for her stance on women's rights. First, "It's none of your business and second, shame on you for interfering," she argued to a male classmate. "We have a fundamental right to choose, without excessive government restriction, so keep your opinions to yourself and practice law!"

In her second year of law school, Supreme Court Justice Ruth Bader Ginsburg was sworn in as a Supreme Court Justice. Frankie earned a spot on the Moot Court Honor Society, rewarded for her oral advocacy and writing skills. Frankie aspired to appear before Her Honor one day, but never had the honor, although she was invited to judge and critique many Moot Court Competitions for law students.

Her third year of law school, Frankie and friends toured DC and The Supreme Court of the United States, the ultimate courtroom. That year, she met her future husband, Tom, on a blind date. She was "rough around the edges," because her dreams of "happily ever after" were shattered twice, jaded and damaged by Dick, but not broken.

Law school guaranteed equality and power for all women, including Frankie. Four years of night school were grueling, but she was relentless in her pursuit of a J.D. and she dreamt of this "rite of passage," from legal secretary to attorney at law. However, equality wasn't so easy to achieve and during her four years of law school, she struggled with intermittent sexist comments, sexual harassment and inequality. Her own classmate, Digby, repeatedly and inappropriately touched her, harassed her, and flirted with her.

A role model to many, he was a disgrace to Frankie. Devastated but not defeated, she shamed the cheaters out loud. "Get your fucking hands off me!" she shouted every time Digby grabbed or kissed her. Embolden, Digby wrote sexually explicit messages and drew naked pictures by her name in the attendance book that passed through the hands of

100 fellow students during Civil Procedure class. She suffered through the touching for two years before meeting Tom. The scoundrel should have been expelled.

"One day, I will fight for the rights of women. Equal and respectful rights. These assholes can't keep getting away with this type of sexual abuse!" she mumbled.

Law School should have been her sanctuary, with equality as the pillar of democracy, but neither law school nor the practice of law ensured that right, so Frankie demanded it. The cheaters weren't expecting Frankie to be stronger, and they didn't know her secret, so they assumed she was easy prey. Looking back on her early years, Frankie would have worn a "Times Up" t-shirt. The classrooms held over 100 students, seated in alphabetic order, which is how she met her lifelong friends, with last names starting with letters M, N, O, P. They had to laugh or they would have cried during those four years, because they feared being called upon to recite IRAC: "Issue, Rule, Analysis, Conclusion," to explain some antiquated case. It included in-your-face, rapid-fire questioning and humiliation.

The terrorizing torts professor called upon Frankie one Saturday morning to recite IRAC. Heart pounding, she nailed it.

"Stand and teach us about Wagon Wheel v. Mavrogan!" She was a tiny beast staring up at Frankie and she barked: "What is the issue, in this case?" Frankie responded, "An invited guest fell while descending a stairway to the Wagon Wheel Saloon and claimed the owner was negligent."

"What is the rule?" "An invitee need not prove the owner's notice of the dangerous condition," she responded.

"What is the analysis, in applying the rule to the facts of the case?" "Knowledge of the dangerous condition is imputed to the owner," she answered.

"What is the conclusion?" "The owner owed a duty to provide safe conditions to the invitee, Mr. Mavrogan," and then it was over. The tiny terror walked away, defeated because she could not stump Frankie, and Frankie was relieved. Time for a break and praise from some friends over coffee.

Over that four-year chunk of her life, Frankie attended baby showers, bridal showers and weddings for classmates and friends. Always the bridesmaid but never the bride, until Tom proposed on New Year's Eve in her third year of law school. Joy and tears led to the Bar Exam and joy and tears followed the Bar Exam. The grueling two-day nightmare was worth every minute. She had to pass so she could plan her wedding. If truth be known, law students, like medical students, are reduced to sleep-deprived night-walkers, hungry, and wandering aimlessly to grab a seat and spill their brain matter all over the exam. Many had to make a mad dash to the lavatory, after being searched by the Moderator.

With all illusions shattered, the questions on the Bar Exam have nothing to do with the practice of law. In fact, the test takers merely memorize general law to rely upon for the legal arguments in court. Walking down the staircase into the bowels of test-taking, Frankie was slapped in the face with reality and anxiety. The closer she got to the exam room, the higher her anxiety rose, as she assumed the other students were smarter than she. "There's the guy who gets straight A's. There's the girl who already has a job. There is the wealthy girl who drives a Mercedes," she noticed.

Packed like a sardine amongst 500 sardines and seated next to a complete stranger, a bluebook lined exam paper was laid on the desk. Frankie pulled out one of her twelve pencils, accidentality stabbed herself with the point and started to answer the first of many essay questions. Unexpectedly, she panicked, threw the pencil down, and froze. As visions of her four-hundred-dollar application fee flooded her thoughts, she grabbed the goddam pencil and feverishly answered the shit out of those essays.

"Drop your pencils" the Moderator commanded and "Hands off your bluebook." "Jesus Christ, I need a double cheeseburger, no onions, extra pickles and fries."

Frankie returned to her hotel room, tossed and turned and didn't sleep a wink. In the morning, descending into the bowels of test takers for the last time, she was armed and ready for the multiple-choice questions.

"Fill in the whole dot, don't miss any portion or you will lose points," she told herself. Pencil points reduced to nubs; the exam was over!

"Drop your pencils and remain seated while your exam books are collected," the Moderator barked, as she congratulated them and said, "That completes the Bar Examination. Good luck everyone."

Her fellow nightwalkers ascended up the stairwell, some crying, others vomiting and more than a few just not giving a damn in that moment. "Time to pack and get out of here," she told Tom. "It was grueling as hell." Now, pleasant thoughts of her wedding replaced the nervousness and the exam nightmares.

She was hired by a law firm in the city, where she worked as she waited for the results to come in. Soon, the next rite of passage arrived: the viewing of the Bar Exam results. She was required to walk ten blocks to City Hall, accompanied by her new employer. Hundreds of exam-takers waited in line to peek inside the leather-bound book for his/her name, although only the names of those who passed were listed.

Following protocol, Frankie approached the leather-bound book, looked down and scrolled to find her name, and then walked away in silence behind the masses. Greeted by the partners waiting for her on the other side of the leather-bound book, she nodded yes, and they headed to a celebratory luncheon.

*"Ahh, lunch with the partners, a secure job for Frankie and the sound of wedding bells!"*

## Chapter 10
### Hood in a Hoodie

*If I can't have her, nobody can have her.*

The phone calls kept coming. First, they started at Simon's office on the answering machine, when Caller ID, area codes or reverse caller look up were not available.

As soon as she heard the first message, "Hi Baby!" chills went up and down her spine.

Frankie was nervous. "He found me! I can't believe he had the nerve to call me here and leave a personal message. He's a monster with no remorse and no shame! I hate him!"

"What do I do? Do I call the police? I can't tell Simon; I have to handle this myself."

Frankie checked the parking lot to ensure Simon had not arrived. "The coast is clear, I better call before he gets here," she thought. She grabbed the phone, dialed Dickhead's number, and let it ring repeatedly.

Getting no answer, relief flooded through her, releasing the anxiety of hearing his voice. She had been distracted with thoughts of the violence and pain but was always reminded of it by the intermittent ringing in her left ear, caused by the cold-cock to her head.

The monster's message said, "Leave a message after the beep." This was her chance to fire back with a threat of having Dick arrested. "I will fucking have you arrested wherever you are, stay away and never come near me!" At that moment, she felt free of fear because in New York, she had backup from lawyers, police, friends and family. The emotional and physical devastation remained hidden in her past. Frankie was never deterred from succeeding in her future.

Over the next four years at Simon's office, she arrived at the office and started her day by retrieving messages from the answering machine. Ready to fight back if she heard that pothead's voice, she pressed "play," closed her eyes and waited for Dick to rear his ugly head again, but he didn't. Now, Frankie felt empowered, fearless against Dick and he didn't like it. After threatening Dick with arrest, he never called the office again. Instead, there were hang-ups on her touch-tone phone at home.

Without ever revealing her story of abuse to Simon, she asked, "Do you know any disgruntled clients who would leave threatening messages?"

"Sure Frankie, all attorneys have disgruntled clients. Don't worry about it, once they get their settlement money, they become grateful clients. I keep a baseball bat under my desk just in case."

She convinced herself, "He is thousands of miles away and he will never show up here. Just in case, I'll leave an aluminum bat under my desk."

Then it followed her home. She caught Her in the act when she picked up the house phone on the first ring.

"Hi Frankie," a female voice said.

Without Caller ID to identify the caller, pissed off, Frankie threw her books down and asked, "Who is this?"

"How's it going Frankie, being back in New York?"

"I'll call the police you creep, who is this?"

"Wow, 'he' did say you were a bitch!"

"Listen, tell him to go to hell!" she shouted. "I will have you arrested asshole, do not ever call this number again!"

"How is law school, Frankie?"

"Tell that prick to rot in hell, I am ending this call!"

The call ended and the hang-ups became few and far between, but she replayed that conversation over and over trying to identify the voice. Maybe it was Kara or perhaps Kara gave Dick her work number, but he already had her home number. That was how he begged for her forgiveness and promised the return of her ring.

Southern Bell Kara was trapped in Dick's web of lies and he had enlisted her to find new prey and track down old prey. Frankie understood it was probably easier for her to do as instructed than standing up to Dick.

Kara called again, this time to meet for dinner because she needed help getting a restraining order. "Of course, I will help you Kara," she said. Simon handled the case and Frankie sat with her in court for support. She held Kara's hand when her batterer showed up for the hearing. She too, had bad taste in men like many successful businesswomen.

"Why are you friends with Dick?"

"You know how it is Frankie, you just can't shake Dick. He needs me if he can't have you," replied Kara.

"You deserve better Kara; Reconcile with the father of your children for their sake! Run like hell from Bad Boy Dick! Run from danger, like I did," warned Frankie.

Kara gave a slight grin and then tears fell down her face.

Over four years of answering Simon's phone and retrieving his messages, there were two more "Hi Baby" messages on the machine, but no sign of Dick.

Never letting her guard down, she constantly looked over her shoulder and strategically placed an aluminum bat on the front seat of her car.

One Wednesday, she left the office, jumped into her car, locked the doors and checked on the bat before her drive to school. Without warning, she saw someone out of the left corner of her eye, and she glanced up. "Oh God, Dick found me, I'm dead," she thought.

A young guy in a black hoodie wearing large sunglasses, grabbed the driver side door handle and tried to get into the car, as Frankie weirdly watching it unfold.

With the two of them staring eye to eye, Frankie calmly asked, "Who sent you?"

Realizing he couldn't get in and now exposed, he nervously muttered, "uh, uh, do you have any money"?

"Who the hell sent you?" Frankie demanded as she grabbed the bat, ready to rumble. This thin young punk was so caught off guard, he took off into the middle of the street.

Slowly, Frankie pulled out of the parking lot, looked both ways and thanked God she had locked the door. On heightened alert because this was not just harassment by phone, she was vigilant, with an emergency plan in place, all times for the next four years, always looking over her shoulder.

Staying in touch with Kara through law school, they met and had several dinners, discussing Kara's legal matters. They never discussed Dick; it was Frankie's rule to never mention his name. Needing free legal advice from Frankie, Kara agreed, except for the times she said, "He still loves you."

After becoming an attorney, Frankie faced threats occasionally, the most notable being Whitefox.

"I am coming to kill her, you tell her that," he instructed Frankie's Office Manager, Reds.

"Frankie, Whitefox said he is coming to kill you!" exclaimed Reds.

"What the hell are you talking about?"

"He called and said he is coming to kill you. Watch your back Frankie!"

Taking no chances, Frankie installed a high-tech alarm system and spotlights at her house, made sure Tom kept his gun nearby and replaced her baseball bat with mace. Always on high alert, Frankie was constantly looking over her shoulder in and out of court.

Still unnerved by crank phone calls, the young punk in the parking lot, Dick at-large and now Whitefox hunting her down, every morning she turned on the spotlights before sunrise. Frankie set up a safety plan with her neighbor, Sully; every morning at 5:30 he toots his horn to acknowledge he is watching on his way out for coffee.

After practicing for several years, Slick found her phone number and called her new law office. "WTF," she thought. She ran to a private phone so no one could hear the conversation.

"Hi, it's Slick. I just want to congratulate on your success. So how are you?"

"I'm great, married, and go to hell," she said as she slammed the phone. "Is he crazy calling me after marrying Lucy and pushing me into the arms of Dick?"

Slick found Frankie on the internet. With no shame, he felt he had the right to speak with her after the trauma he caused. He called two more times and each time, Frankie ran to the phone and hung up immediately.

"Why do these assholes call me?" Move on or go to hell, she thought.

She continued to check on Kara to make sure she and the children were safe and always encouraging her to work on her family.

"Let's have dinner again, Frankie. I have more questions and need your help with a plan for reconciliation."

"Sure, let's meet at the Thai Restaurant down the street from you, Kara".

"Poor Southern Belle Kara and the kids," Frankie thought as she let out a sigh.

"Sure, see you at 6:00 on Friday night, park around back and I'll park beside you so we can walk in together," said Kara.

"That's weird," she thought "She better not be bringing Dick with her. I will smash his skull with my bat if he comes near me."

With sweaty palms, Frankie pulled into the parking lot and kept her hand on the bat. "What a dangerous spot, I hope Kara is ok. I hope Whitefox doesn't show up, he could be following me."

"I don't see her car, but I don't want to be alone in the parking lot. Think I'll go inside, and she can find me there," she strategized. Before she was out of the car, the punk in the hoodie again approached her and stood over her before she could get out of the car. Full of rage and fear, she grabbed the bat and cracked him across the knees, screaming for help and beeping her horn. The punk fell to the ground screaming, "You bitch, I'll kill you!"

Frankie stood there paralyzed with fear. "OMG! OMG!" was all she could utter.

A Good Samaritan called the police when he heard the horn going off. Witnesses ran to the car and told the police what they saw.

"Who are you?" Frankie shouted.

As they pulled him to his feet, the police took down his hoodie and removed his sunglasses. "Ma'am, do you know her?"

"Her?"

Frankie couldn't believe her eyes. Shaky and with a heavy heart, Frankie identified Kara as the hooded punk, sweet southern belle Kara.

"Dick loves you. You don't deserve him, he's mine!"

"I'll be back bitch!" Kara said, mascara running down her face. "I made all the calls to your office, your house, and I tried to rob you that day in the parking lot."

"Fuck you, Kara! Thanks for the confessions!"

"Did you get all of that officer?" asked Frankie as she wiped the tears from her eyes and said, "I want her charged with all of that!"

"Yes ma'am," the officer responded.

### *Chapter 11*
Dreams Do Come True

*"Melt that junk down and use the gold and diamonds for my engagement ring!"*

Dick assumed buying her gifts of adoration would help Frankie forget Slick. During the courting phase, which was going far too quickly for her liking, he asked her to meet him at the jeweler. He wanted to give her a ring, proof to all, she belonged only to him. Frankie had dreams of the 'right man' and being loved. Perhaps, this would make her finally feel worthy of someone's undivided attention and affection.

Dick's abuse looked like love to her, disguised by caring and protection from the painful breakup with Slick. He didn't let her feel the loss of good times or allow the feeling of loneliness. He replaced them with newer and happier memories; he force-fed Frankie when she was hungry for love.

With no choice but to move forward with Dick, who was clearly obsessed with her, she rushed to the jewelers. "He must love me if he wants everyone to know we are a couple, and I am his. No one has said that to me. Slick only gave me a heart-shaped pendant after he cheated. Bet he had a case of them to string along his prey." Tragically, Dick was so cunning, clever and manipulative, she didn't realize how bad things were until she was broken and drowning in despair.

Later in life, weighing the evidence of 'love' Dick showed her with the ring, and Slick with the necklace, the red flags were revealed, but she realized it too late. Frankie was naïve in those days and nothing to measure what true love meant.

The first time Dick strangled her at his house, she had thrown the ring at him before she escaped. During his manipulative phone call, begging for forgiveness and another chance, he used the ring as reconciliation bait.

"If you come back to me, you can have the ring," he said. Frankie didn't care about the goddamn ring. She wanted to get out of San Francisco and should have stood her ground. She ignored all the red flags, knew she deserved better, but she let her dreams of a future nearly destroy her present.

After Frankie had tossed Dick out of the apartment, he demanded the ring back in retaliation. Stronger and ready to fight back, she chuckled and packed it in a velvet black box with candy. To prepare for the showdown, she put on makeup and did her hair. With one last look in the mirror, she could hear Dick's incessant screaming, like a child throwing a tantrum... "Get the fuck down here, you bitch!"

She was calm inside, for she knew this was the end. He was standing outside the gate and Frankie was inside, safe. She had taken the keys away from him to prevent him gaining access to the apartment or outside area. She dragged out his wait, riding the elevator down the four flights, letting others on to join her going up or down. As the elevator opened on the first floor, she thought "Showtime" as she faced a belligerent Dick, whose face was pushed up against the gate, hands straining to reach her without success. For reasons unknown, his co-worker, Ricky, was with him as if he needed a witness.

"I'll kill you; I'll fucking kill you!" he shouted angrily. Afraid of being grabbed or spit on, she threw the small package through the gate, like a zookeeper throwing a slab of meat to a hungry lion. Dick was humiliated when the former neighbors recognized him, seeing him on the outside of the gate begging. No one gave a damn, not even Ricky, who had to drag him away. She should have called the police, had him arrested and charged with aggravated assault, terroristic threats, attempted murder via strangulation. She didn't dare look back, she wanted nothing more to do with him. Now, her goal was to teach others about the severity and dangers that need to be addressed and the red flags thrown your way in order to stay alive.

Calmly, head held high, Frankie turned and walked away towards the koi pond, her face getting splashed by the fountain. The landlord cheered her, acknowledging her courage, her newfound freedom, and, most of all, Dick would no longer be inviting a drug dealer into the building.

"Good for you, Frankie!" her friend, Pyper, cheered when Frankie finally shared her story. "You stood up to the bastard!"

"Yeah, it felt good to turn my back on him and he couldn't get to me," Frankie replied.

"Holy shit, Frankie, you had the strength all along. You did your best, but you didn't know he was a narcissist, lacked empathy and you were in a superficial and exploitive relationship." Not everyone in this type of relationship is lucky. We have to see the signs and watch for red flags, overcome the self-denial before it's too late.

"I was too young to understand it all," she whispered, as she sipped from her "Times Up" mug.

Before she left San Francisco, he invited her for burger and fries; it was the 'least' he could do before disappearing forever. He had the nerve to hand me the velvet package with the ring and offered an empty apology! Maybe he was using it to bait me to go back. That is when Frankie knew inside, she was free of him. They said their goodbyes, had a quick hug and she walked back to the apartment to start her new journey.

Frankie returned home to fulfill two dreams, first to practice law and the second to fall in love. Well aware both required a long journey; she had a lifetime to travel both roads. Determined, she would never give up on either dream. With her pursuit of love secondary to the primary quest of her Doctor of Jurisprudence, she relied on match-making and blind dates set up by her childhood friends and classmates. There weren't any eligible bachelors at school, day students were too young, and the night students married. Attempts by classmates or friends felt like trying to fit a square peg into a round hole. Nothing felt right. Reluctantly, she tried the dance floor again, to discover it felt outdated and held too many painful memories.

She was rarely a bridesmaid because of her matter-of-fact and truthful approach to life. She never attempted to catch the bridal bouquets at family or friends' weddings. It was obnoxious for her to watch desperate women fight over flowers and fall as cheap shoes hit the shiny, slippery dance floor. Rolling her eyes at their desperation, she knew inside, there was someone special for her.

Frankie knew she deserved better and would not settle for anything other than her Cinderella story, after living a similar story as the middle child, overshadowed by the "Princess and the Baby."

She discovered San Franciscans were far more tolerant and open to new ideas and different lifestyles compared to her native New Yorkers. She didn't struggle to fit in upon her return. She already stood out, and some didn't like it. She ignored the neighborhood gossip about her breakups, and the jealousy about her success. Her childhood friends from the neighborhood, Santo and Jay, remained steadfast supporters and loyal friends. That was a good feeling.

Santo, the boy-next door, was encouraged by his mother to marry Frankie because of her Catholic upbringing and good girl behaviors. Both sets of parents were in collusion on the lifelong plan. It didn't happen because bad-girl, Lee-Lee, stole Santo and trapped him into marriage with her high school pregnancy. Lee-Lee was one of the bullies in the alley, who followed her into high school before Cookie shut it down.

Sitting on the steps of her parents' rowhome, Frankie was studying and working on her tan when Santo approached her and sat next to her.

"Welcome home. How is school going?" he asked. "It's tough, but it will be worth it," she admitted. After they caught up on family, work and other topics, Frankie asked, "Can you help me find a car for work and school? It's an hour's drive each way and I don't want to drive the brown grandmom-mobile anymore."

Santo giggled as he said, "I know. I saw you driving it back and forth while trying to find a parking spot for the 'big old boat'."

"I know what I am looking for, a black two-door sedan with a car payment of $200 per month. Do you have anything on your lot where you work?" she inquired.

He smiled and said, "Yeah, call my friend Tom. He will help you find what you are looking for and he is a really nice guy." Little did Frankie know Santo had something up his sleeve.

Desperate not to drive the grand mom-mobile her parents' lent her, she called Tom and gave him the specs. He searched for the car and price she wanted, calling weekly with updates until he found the car for her. During the weeks he searched, Frankie continued her own search for a husband. Tom wasn't even in the running.

Confident, Frankie searched for a successful man, but was ready to remain single and successful on her own.

On the last update call regarding the search for Frankie's car, Tom said, "I found your car! I want to take you to see it." Suspicious, she asked, "Why? I can check it out myself." He giggled and said, "I'll pick you up at 6:30, so you can take a test drive." Her suspicion intensified as he said, "See you Friday at 6:30. Santo gave me your address."

As soon as they hung up, Frankie called Santo immediately, upset knowing Tom knew where she lived. Santo calmly confirmed what Tom had said and reassured her he was a great guy. She had nothing to worry about. Frankie felt differently but agreed to meet him to get her car.

Unsure of Tom's agenda, and the reasoning behind his kindness and willingness to go the extra mile, her suspicions were at an all-time high. She had to figure out how to set aside her fear and ignore her jaded self to buy the goddam car. Watching the "Dating Game," the doorbell rang and Frankie ran to the front door. She peeked out the window and didn't recognize the man. She asked her sister to stand close by in the event of potential danger and opened the door. "Can I help you?" she asked.

He responded, "I'm Tom. See, it's on my name tag."
He chuckled.

Tom was a charming, dark and handsome hunk with
a full mustache and dimples. Thrilled and nervous, she turned
to her sister, behind the door, and whispered, "He is so hot!
I'll call you if he tries to kidnap me." She threw quarters in
her purse for a payphone.

Why didn't Santo tell her? she wondered. Later, she
learned Santo had been setting them up because he knew they
would make a great couple. She deserved better than she had
in the past, and Santo knew Tom well.

"Where is your car?" she asked. He escorted her to a
pearly white Mitsubishi 3000 GT sports car and held the door
open for her.

Is this really happening? A six-foot-two handsome
man with a beautiful smile and dimples, in an expensive sports
car, all in one night, she thought, pinching herself gently.
She couldn't believe it was happening. A dream comes
true!Frankie was caught up in this unbelievable 'set up'.

As they sat side by side, they couldn't take their eyes
off each other; one caught the other taking a peek while
the other looked away, feigning disinterest. She asked after
a while, "Why are we going so far away for a car?" Tom
replied, "So I can get to know you. Santo set us up, didn't you
know?" Frankie hadn't a clue until that moment, and she was
grateful for this wonderful gift from Santo but she was not
about to give it away, yet.

They arrived at the dealership and jumped into Frankie's dream car for a test drive, with Tom at the wheel. They headed for the nearby woods. Night was falling, and it was getting darker the further they drove into the woods. Tom stopped the car abruptly. Frankie became alarmed and in a very bravado voice asked, "Are you kidnapping me?"

Giggling again, he looked into her eyes, and said, "I'm going to check under the hood before you buy it." He got out of the car, and actually did check under the hood. Frankie was relieved and also somewhat pissed. Why would someone check under the car now, why not before? She held her guard up and prayed she would be fine.

That was the first of many nights she had with her knight in shining armor. On the long road home one day, Tom asked her, "What do you want in a man?"

Fresh out of a contract class, Frankie stated matter-of-factly her terms: "I want a two-karat diamond ring; I am keeping my maiden name to honor my father; and absolutely no children." Tom counteroffered, "OK, a two-karat diamond ring; you can keep your maiden name, honoring your father; but I do want one child." Frankie smiled ear to ear, shaking hands to seal the deal.

Her professor had taught in class a contract requires offer, consideration and acceptance. The two accepted the other's terms and sealed the deal after the handshake, their first kiss, in the front seat of Tom's car.

Scheduling dates weren't easy with Frankie's busy
school schedule and Tom's twelve-hour workdays. They made
it work: Wednesday nights, after class, they met at a diner for
blueberry pie and French fries. Sundays, they ate pasta at her
parents' house, with an occasional dinner out. They dated
for two years and attended a New Year's Eve Gala yearly,
replacing the nightmarish Gala she attended in San Francisco.
Friends, family, classmates were thrilled for Frankie. Even
her parents gave their approval and loved Tom. His parents,
not so much. They loved Tom and made it work. Both sets of
parents had attended the same school, grew up in the same
neighborhood, and shared the same ethnic culture. She finally
had her "plus one" for parties, weddings and school events.
She found her protector, with a soft side. Yes, her steadfast
dream was coming true.

She fell in love with him during their long drives.
On one drive, she asked nonchalantly, "Do you yell?" He
chuckled and said, "I don't yell." Right then, she knew he
was the one for her. I hope he loves me, she thought. They
continued to date for many months, neither of them ever
saying, "I love you." They took their time until the right
moment, which happened on a drive in the Mitsubishi.
When will he propose, Frankie wondered? She wasn't finished
with law school yet and still had the Bar Exam to take. Tom
was understanding and patient about it all.

It was the third New Year's Eve Gala they were
attending as a couple. As they arrived at the hotel, Frankie
hoped this would be the night Tom would "pop" the question.

Unbeknownst to her, both families knew it was coming and had made their individual arrangements to congratulate the couple at midnight via phone.

After a decadent dinner at the hotel, her Cinderella moment arrived at midnight. As the ball dropped, Tom knelt on one knee, and with a two-karat diamond in hand, proposed to Frankie. Excited, in shock, and ready for her dream to come true, she said, "Of course I will... YES!"

A romantic toast of champagne was followed by phone calls to their respective parents, sharing the joyful news. She told Tom, "Let the wedding plans begin after I pass the Bar Exam."

On the bulletin board in her childhood bedroom hung a magazine picture of a sleek, cream-colored wedding gown, embellished with pearls and sequins. After four years of law school, the day arrived when she could finally pull the shiny picture off the board. She was ready to search for her dream gown at the bridal salons.

Armed with her wedding-planning binder, she headed down the highway in the shiny black Honda Tom had waxed for her the night before. Alone, she drove to the first bridal salon, with trepidation and ready for the challenge.

She pulled into the parking lot, her heart pounding. Double checking to ensure the magazine photo of her dream gown was inside the binder, as she got out of the car and headed to the door. She heard a bell ring as she entered the salon and was greeted by Lana, the bridal consultant. Frankie had dreamt of this day for so long and in "Frankie fashion" she was going to enjoy the moment, alone, with a three-way mirror, a bridal consultant, no judgements from mom or sisters.

"Let's get your measurements, Frankie, and we will go from there," Lana said. "Sounds good Lana. Can I show you my dream gown?" whispered Frankie excitedly. She pulled out the photo from the binder and handed it to Lana.

"Of course. I will look for your dream gown and pull a few others to give you options." Frankie was seated in an ornate, red velvet chair, and was handed a mimosa to sip while she waited for the gowns. Lana returned shortly, with six gowns and veils: some slim fitted, some poufy and the dream gown on the top. "I am glad I could find it, Frankie. Try the others on first, save it for last" Following instructions, she tried on the first five with an open mind, gazing into the mirror, twirling like Cinderella before the ball. As she was preparing to try on the dream gown, it hit her.... after all these years, the gown is here, in this very room with me! Is this a dream, or a dream come true?

Lana helped her into the gown, clipped the back to fit perfectly. "Turn around, Frankie. Look at the mirror." Frankie turned around slowly; train attached at the back of her waist. "This is my dream gown," she softly whispered. She looked at her engagement ring, then back at her reflection, and soaked it all in.

"Time to add the veil," Lana said.

"Can I see a tiara, instead?"

Lana left briefly, returning with a tiara in hand, and

placed it on Frankie's head, adjusting her long locks of curls to lie on her shoulders. "Turn around again, Frankie. What do you see?"

"It's perfect, just as I dreamt years ago when I saw it in the magazine."

"We wish you all the happiness in the world. You deserve it." After a quick hug, Lana and Frankie parted ways until the gown and tiara arrived.

The wedding day was the following June. The mansion was decorated with fresh purple, pink, and white flowers. The gazebo where the union of Frankie and Tom was to take place was adorned with white lilies, white tulips, and ivy. The makeup artist and hair stylist arrived at the same time as the bridal party. It was surreal, a mix of fact and fantasy, just like Young Frankie imagined while reading the fairy tale.

She watched the ring bearer and flower girl chase each other, stopping to snack on French fries. They ran by the pond filled with ducks and ducklings.

His Honor, who had recommended Frankie to the Public Defender for her brilliant mind, arrived and greeted Tom. As she watched this monumental moment, she saw His Honor hand Tom a shot of bourbon, saying, "Tom, you will need this to get through the ceremony." Frankie chuckled as she watched the two of them walk down the path to the gazebo.

The hair stylist and makeup artist had done their jobs, glamorously transforming Frankie and her court. It was time for pictures. "Here comes the Father of the Bride," said the photographer.

Now it's real. It's my turn to walk with dad, Frankie thought as she heard the first few notes of the "Wedding March." She took her father's arm, and together they walked down the pathway, past the ducks, the pond full of lily pads, the guests, arriving at the gazebo, where a handsome Tom waited for her. Her father turned to Tom. Shaking hands before he gave Frankie away, he said to Tom, "Take care of her."

The two of them turned to face His Honor, smiling from ear to ear. They listened as her classmate Genevie and her husband, Myles, sing "Ave Maria," while every Italian cried. His Honor stood under the gazebo, facing the invited guests, and began the ceremony. She closed her eyes and thought, 'My guests are finally seeing my dream fulfilled, after all the years of trauma I went through.'

" I now pronounce you, man and wife. You may kiss the bride." Frankie had waited twenty-five years for this magical moment. (At the time of this writing, they will celebrate their twenty-fifth anniversary.)

The guests cheered loudly for them as they led the way to the ballroom, as rose petals fell like a snow flurry from above. After greeting the guests and the end of the bridal party introductions, everyone was seated. Tom and Frankie took to the dance floor and called Santo to join them. He was introduced, thanked and praised for bringing the newlyweds together. The crowd cheered for him, some knew him as the boy-next door, and others for finding Prince Charming. Frankie gave him a big hug before letting him leave the dance floor.

Several toasts later, Frankie and Tom had their first dance to "I Finally Found Someone." She had hoped and prayed it would happen and never gave up. She had endured pain before finding her Mr. Right. In her journey she discovered one has to respect and protect themselves before they can find their special someone.

For the father and daughter dance, Frankie and her dad took to the dance floor with "Isn't She Lovely." When it was over, her father kissed her on the cheek. The party started, with everyone dancing the night away. Surrounded by loved ones, new friends, classmates, former employers, it was an event to cherish.

Frankie did keep her maiden name, and they had one child. Frankie got her "knight in shining armor" and a "little knight." As long as one does not give up and avoids being stuck in patterns or cycles, dreams can come true. Look in the right places, ask for help and help others.

Ironically, Frankie now plays a role as damage control in divorce matters. It's a paradigm, a pattern she relives every day with a different outcome for each client, and a broken fairytale for all.

## *Chapter 12*
## Locked in a Cell

*Disgusted by the facts revealed*

After her Summer Internship ended, His Honor
said, "Frankie, come in here and have a seat for your final
evaluation." He was stern, with a husky voice and used to the
"goof old boy ways." He looked up, put his cigarette down
and as the smoke came her way, he said, "Frankie, you are
aggressive and talented. The Public Defender's Office needs
you," he added as he handed her a job application, which she
gladly accepted. Frankie stood up, shook His Honor's hand
and thanked him. Not since those words of confidence from
Portia and Victor had she received such a compliment.

Frankie wasn't expecting the compliment because
the other Intern, Alfie, had commanded all of His Honor's
attention with his deep voice, private school education and
his chain smoking. Alfie marginalized Frankie and criticized

her work throughout her internship, always bragging he was a criminal defense attorney, and her legal briefs were sub-par and her legal research inadequate. "Do I have to put up with this sexist bullshit besides Digby's wandering hands," she thought.

On that day, Alfie overheard the entire conversation with His Honor. In fact, he looked on from his desk across the room and witnessed Frankie's shining moment. Frankie walked past Alfie, waving her job application and boasted, "See you at the P.D.'s Office."

She walked to the Office of the Public Defender with her completed Application for Employment and scheduled her interview for the following day. She recognized "the" Public Defender, he too had a raspy smoker's voice like His Honor and lit a cigar up during the interview. Like in an old fifty's movie, he leaned back in his oversized leather chair, put his feet on the desk and said through the cloud of smoke, "I reviewed your application and your work experience, very impressive."

"Thank you," Frankie sheepishly said.

"You come highly recommended by His Honor. When can you start?"

"Immediately," she responded.

Within days, Frankie reported for duty and was escorted to an office by her "roommate," a veteran attorney named Sterling, a short, kind-hearted giggler with unrelenting wit. "Thank God he was nothing like Alfie and thank God Alfie isn't my roommate," she thought.

After a guided tour of the Office of the Public Defender, she was gifted with a copy of the Crimes Code and the Motor Vehicle Code. Assistant Public Defender (APD) Frankie was glowing and set out for a shopping spree to add conservative suits and sensible heels to navigate prisons and holding cells. APD Frankie was assigned to the minor courts, where the defendant had his/her first hearing. The holding cell was not an easy adjustment, and the smell could knock any pregnant woman off her feet.

During her training with Sterling, the dynamic duo were assigned the most heinous of defendants, although it wasn't a shock to either of them. Even with Sterling accompanying her to the cell, one shackled prisoner snuck up from behind her, sniffed her hair as the others smirked, saying nothing. Disgusted, Frankie banged on the metal, double fisted, until the Constable set her free. "What's up with the guy smelling hair and what is my recourse," she demanded. The Constable calmed her down and said, "You're too old for him, he's a pedophile."

As she arrived at the courtroom, the Constable pointed her to the witness stand, where a young girl holding a teddy bear faced the pedophile prisoner who had molested her. The bastard forced her to face him, and not surprisingly, Whitefox's attorney, Attorney Ima Trator, represented the pedophile.

Undeterred by creepy holding cells and touchy prisoners, she continued to defend justice during pregnancy. Now pregnant, nauseous and wearing too-tight heels, she drove from court to court, five days per week, vomiting in private, and compensating with ice cream.

One Thursday, she was assigned twin brothers, Bobby and Buddy, both in their 60's, who shared the same cell and lots of perverted secrets. She interviewed them separately, on opposite sides of the cell, although neither acknowledged the other, as if they were complete strangers. The near-catatonic twins were both facing rape charges, but under very distinct and diabolic circumstances.

Bobby was accused of raping an elderly woman, a wheelchair-bound amputee, who could not ambulate without the assistance of a care-giver. "How horrific," Frankie thought. "I'm not gonna win this one." Never-the-less, she took pen to paper and outline her cross-examination for the victim, although it was sketchy.

Now stuck beside him on a hard, wood bench, he relayed his version of the facts as Frankie took copious notes, sometimes highlighting them to prove her concern. "She wanted me bad," he boasted. "She is a neighbor at my apartment complex, two doors down the hallway and she was always flirting with me in the elevator." He continued, without an invitation, "She showed up at my place and rang my buzzer at about 7:00 PM, but I couldn't' hear the buzzer or let her in because I was in the shower."

"Then, she opened my door and rolled in unannounced," he stated, as if he was credible. "She must have heard the shower running, so with no shame, she rolled that wheelchair right up to my bathroom, peeked in, ripped the shower curtain open and demanded sex from me," he alleged with dead eyes.

"Are you fucking kidding me," Frankie thought as she dropped her pen. Holding herself back from ripping up her notes, she was called to the courtroom. She has to pass the State Trooper and take the walk of shame. He judged her, "How dare you represent that scumbag," he whispered in her ear. Unshaken by his attempt at intimidation, APD Frankie took copious notes during the victim's testimony and held her pen tight, in case she needed to stab Bobby in self-defense!

The testimony revealed the eighty-year-old Velma, a poor helpless woman, went to Bobby's apartment to deliver her renowned meatloaf and mashed potatoes with gravy. She didn't "want him," she was just a nice church lady performing a good deed, but she was ambushed by a rapist.

During her testimony, she alleged he let her in, then led her to his bedroom where he grabbed her from her wheelchair and threw her onto his bed, where she had no chance of escape. She further alleged he covered her mouth first, punched her in the face, causing a blowout fracture and multiple contusions, still evident on her face.

Disgusted by the facts revealed and the evidence presented, Frankie was still required to make a bail argument to get him out of jail, which was adamantly denied, in the face of Bobby's violent and deviant behavior. His Honor looked at Bobby, pounded the gavel and held a crime had been committed and, more likely, Bobby had committed the crime. Immediately, he was dragged back to the cell by the Constable to await his fate but showed no remorse nor shame. The Trooper grinned and pointed his finger at Frankie.

Frankie had to regroup, start over with her notes and await Buddy's arrival. He was escorted from the cell. She heard the clanging of shackles being dragged down the hall and it was "go time," round two for her. After seating Buddy beside her, the arresting officers were determined to find out whether the tall blond victim was a man or a woman, as they looked her up and down.

Buddy alleged he picked up a woman at his local "dive-bar" on Karaoke night. After some flirting, some singing and several drinks, he invited her home for "some fun in the hot tub." She accepted the invitation, and he grabbed her hand as they walked into Buddy's rancher, located on a wooded lot. Leading her through the house on a guided tour like a realtor, Buddy bragged about his new hot tub, where the tour ended. After turning on the jets and checking the temperature, they both climbed into the bubbles.

While his hand was exploring Sheila's body through the bubbles, Buddy determined she did not have "woman parts."

Frankie asked, "What did you say"?

He shouted, "She has to pay for her lie because she is a man, and I was looking for a woman." He added, "I bought drinks for a woman, kissed a woman, and I wanted a woman in my goddam hot tub." He appeared shaken by the series of events, although he tried to murder Sheila because she "wronged him."

Enraged by touching a man's private parts, he jumped out of the hot tub and grabbed his weedwhacker. He ripped out the wire, caught her, wrapped the wire around her neck and pulled tight until blood ran down her neck. Undeterred by the blood and evidence which could be used against him, he pulled tight until she fought back and screamed for help.

Help was on the way because Buddy's neighbors had called the police. Startled by the sirens, Buddy made a mad dash for a hiding spot in his shed, where he hid naked, except for his ratty old shoes and holding the blood stained weedwhacker. The police searched outside and could see his feet from under the shed door. They broke down the door and wrestled him to the ground, after they confiscated the weed wacker. As he was dragged away in a hospital gown offered by the EMT's, he passed Sheila on a gurney in the ambulance.

After that riveting testimony, Frankie stood and said, "No questions Your Honor. Defendant remains silent and will proceed at time of trial." She made a bail argument, which was immediately denied. His Honor looked at Buddy, pounded the gavel and held a crime had been committed and, more likely, Buddy had committed that crime. Immediately, Buddy was dragged back to the cell, still enraged.

Frankie ignored the comments of the officers on her walk of shame, turned and said, "Shame on you." With her brief case loaded and her head full of deviant behavior that violated the social norms, she got the hell out of there, holding her head high. Both Bobby and Buddy were held for trial, and Frankie made the front page of the newspaper. Although it wasn't a proud moment, she proved she was tougher than most, strong enough to sit in a locked cell with two accused rapists.

## *Chapter 13*
### Facing the Beast

*Sit tight and wait for my text*

Jackie wiped the blood off her face, iced her black eye, scrubbed the blood stains off her jeans, and dragged herself to seek prosecution of the beast.

Beautiful, twenty-something year-old, olive-skinned Jackie proved to be strong enough to report the beatings to the police, to the court and to Frankie. On the way to the Halls of Justice, overcome with fear, she couldn't face him or tell her terrifying and traumatizing story.

Frankie prepared for Jackie's hearing, her first in the role of attorney, armed with attitude and rage. Teary-eyed and shaky, Jackie slowly walked beside her, neither of them ready to face the beast. She wasn't prepared for the flood of emotion that would consume her, but she had to be a warrior for Jackie.

Jackie reluctantly handed Frankie the photographic evidence of the aftermath of his savage attack, proof the beast had grabbed her by the throat, threw her face first into the front steps and stomped on her back. Frankie stared at the photos as they walked two blocks, horrified by Jackie's bloody nose, black eye, and the defined shape of the beast's boot mark on her back.

It was time to protect Jackie and to make sure she would not come face to face with him. Frankie strategically escorted her to a conference room.

"Sit tight and wait for my text message with instructions and dial 911 if you see him," she instructed.

Jackie nodded yes, looked down and held her phone tightly, while Frankie ran to the courtroom to assume her place for the call of the list by His Honor. She waited for an hour until Jackie's case was called, but the beast failed to appear.

His Honor said, "Well, do you want me to issue a bench warrant for his arrest, or do you want a hearing?" "My client demands a hearing, Your Honor." Then, frantically, she sent a text to Jackie, and met her at the entrance to the courtroom.

"Don't panic, stay fearless for Jackie," she commanded herself.

Then she stepped on the long, red carpet to face his Honor on the bench, and recognized it wasn't about her. A warrior for others now, she was strong enough to do it, and was meant to do it.

The remaining onlookers stared silently as Frankie and Jackie walked down the long, red carpet to the exit as they awaited their turn for justice.

Frankie walked tall and proud, past all 100 of them. She stood up to the beast, who was too weak and too cowardly to face them in court.

Jackie broke down and cried. "You're okay," Frankie told her. "He can't come near you or the baby, or he goes to jail. Call the police if he shows up!"

Thirty years ago, Frankie was in Jackie's shoes, not the warrior standing beside her in heels, and no one ever knew. It's a tragedy you don't see it coming; there are no rules, and it can happen to anyone.

## Chapter 14
### Caught on Tape

No one had heard from Molly for two days, New Year's Eve and New Year's Day.

Forty-eight hours of unanswered calls had Molly's parents worried. They had witnessed tirades and violent episodes at the hands of their son-in-law, Marty. They knew he was capable of anything, including killing himself and taking the family with him.

In desperation, Molly's parents reached out to her brother, Steve, to check on the family. They needed and wanted answers. Arriving at the house, Steve went to the front door, pounding with both fists, shouting Molly's name. Unsuccessful at getting any response, he went around the house, peeking into windows, his investigation going nowhere.

"Please, please, please let them be ok. Let Marty be gone forever," he hoped. Feeling helpless and not giving up, he ran to his pickup truck and called the State Police. He sat in the truck, waiting for "backup," shotgun on his lap. He didn't call their parents yet, uncertain as to what to tell them.

"Hurry Trooper, hurry dude, I don't know how much time they have left," he muttered to himself. Finally, the Trooper rolled up in his cruiser, no sirens, and looked around from the car. There wasn't any sense of urgency in his movements, as the trooper got out of his car. Wearing a bullet-proof vest, Taser and service pistol, Steve expected more urgency, but didn't see it.

"What the hell?!" Steve thought, "My sister could be dead. What's with the attitude? Is his give a dam busted?" He jumped out of his truck, without the shotgun for fear of being shot himself, guided the Trooper up the driveway and pointed to the front door. After explaining the family crisis and describing Marty's dangerous episodes, Steve was forced to return to the pickup to wait with bated breath. He did as he was told, and sat in his truck, holding the shotgun.

"Molly and the kids will be saved. Marty better not be in there," Steve hoped. "Goddam brother-in-law!"

Trooper Lilyliver pounded on the front door, and this time, Marty answered. Calmly, he opened the door and welcomed the Trooper into the house. Escorted by Marty, the six-foot-two beefy trooper was guided into living room and offered a cup of coffee.

"Everything ok here?" Lilyliver inquired, as the questioning commenced. Marty was as cool as a cucumber as the trooper pounded on the door, warning Molly and the kids to "Shut the fuck up, make no movements and or sounds. If I hear anything or you tip off this cop, I will kill your mother!"

"Yeah, just rung in the new year. My wife took the kids shopping, since everything they wanted for Christmas is on sale today, LOL," he chuckled.

"Thanks for the coffee. Here is my card, in case you need it."

"Yes, sir and thank you for coming out on a holiday. Happy New Year Officer!"

Being charmed by Marty, standing only his boxers and a t-shirt, not in the least suspicious of the ensemble, Lilyliver took notes, shook Marty's hand and returned to his cruiser. He told Steve there was nothing to be concerned about as his sister and kids had gone shopping. Steve had no other option, than to leave, praying Molly and the kids were indeed shopping.

Molly heard the ridiculous man-cave-like conversation while trapped in the kitchen with the children, holding their hands over their mouths to ensure compliance with Marty's demands.

For hours, he had falsely imprisoned the family, then grabbed Molly by the throat and strangled her. Full of rage and eager to kill her, Marty snatched the answering machine out of the wall and tied her hands together with the cord.

The "mastermind" hadn't noticed the answering machine turned on and taped the whole psychotic ordeal; the threat to kill Molly, the screams of his children, Sage and Heather. On and on the ordeal went but no neighbors or help came, until Lilyliver showed up, who ignored the protocol for investigating Steve's report. He didn't interrogate Marty or ask if he owned a weapon. He never called for backup so he could investigate the scene, search for weapons or search for Molly and the kids.

If protocol had been followed, he would have heard Molly's gurgling caused by Marty's fat, ham hands around her throat. Molly could have revealed Marty had held a pot of hot coffee over her head, with the steam rising above and into the air, before he offered some to the Trooper. All of it, the sobbing and screaming of Sage and Heather, Molly begging for her life and the wife beater's violent rampage were captured on a tiny cassette tape in the answering machine on the floor, unnoticed by Lilyliver or Marty.

The following week, Frankie received a call from Molly. "I think my husband should be arrested; can you help me?"

"Molly, what are you talking about?"?

"My husband attacked me and held me down on the floor, with the kids watching but the police didn't arrest him."

"Where are the kids?" "They're in school." "Where is your husband?" "I don't know."

"Ok, grab your purse and your cell phone, have your mother pick up the kids and drive to the courthouse now.

They have a Domestic Violence Advocate available to meet with you and to file a Restraining Order against him. Don't think, just drive, Molly! Tell them everything that happened and call me when you get the Order!"

Given the horrific facts and circumstances presented to the court, Molly was granted a Temporary Restraining Order, which she faxed to Frankie as they prepared for the hearing. Marty was evicted from the house and barred from any contact with his wife and/or his children. He ended up living with his parents in a house full of guns.

Molly delivered the "smoking gun," the cassette tape, to Frankie's office. While she was listening to the tape and preparing direct and cross-examination, she received a call from Marty's attorney, Ms. Muddie. After brief introductions, a heated discussion ensued. "You can't use the tape in court counsel, it violates the Wire Tap Act."

"Incorrect Muddie! It's admissible because there was no expectation of privacy when Marty strangled his wife and threatened to pour hot coffee on her, while Sage and Heather watched. The children became third party witnesses to a heinous crime and your client turned on the answering machine during his fit of rage."

"Listen to the goddam tape and hear your client screaming as my client is gasping for air, the children watching in terror," she added. "If you really believe the children were not harmed by watching that violent rampage, then hang up your law license," Counsel wouldn't acknowledge the truth, so Frankie headed to the courtroom with Molly and the children and ran into the Trooper.

Frankie cornered him, with his Subpoena in hand, and said, "I have this cassette tape to present to Her Honor, which Marty taped and has all of the damning evidence I need to win this hearing." With her mini-cassette player in hand, she played the tape of Molly's gurgling and the children screaming, for the Trooper. "Here is my evidence. What will be your testimony?" Dumbfounded, he said, "I didn't see or hear anything! I swear!" "That's because you were chatting with the batterer, who sustained a severe brain injury that resulted in recurring violence, instead of surveying the permitter of the home, right?"

"Listen to the full recording and let me know what your testimony would be if I called you to testify." she commanded. As he started to sweat, the Trooper defensively responded, "I didn't know."

"Well, now you do," Frankie mumbled and continued "Now, I am going in there to present my case to that grumpy judge and the truth will be told by Molly and the children." After sharing the recording with the children's court appointed child advocate, he and Frankie were in alliance against Muddie, as the Trooper stood helpless and ashamed outside the courtroom.

Donning her infamous blond striped bangs, Her Honor summoned all counsel and warned them, the Trooper and the parties she wanted to get started because she had already waited an hour, while counsel discussed the case. She shouted, "Get ready to call your first witness Frankie or make a deal now!" Frazzled by those instructions and full of shit, Marty's attorney caved and agreed to a two-year stay-away order.

"Write it up in your handwriting and recommend your client sign it!" Frankie demanded.

As a unified front, Frankie, Marty's attorney, Muddie, and the Trooper stood before Her Honor, and waited for her to comply. Now, the tough part, drag Marty in to agree to the stay-away terms and to sign it.

Muddie knew better, so she approached him and said, "They have a tape of what you did to your wife and kids. I recommend you sign this or face that angry judge. Further, the Trooper can use this testimony against you at a criminal hearing. Review and sign it!"

The monster was brought to his knees that morning, sobbing and shaking, while outnumbered by the "good guys," his in-laws and his children.

"Wipe your tears and face the judge for what you did," Frankie thought.

After they walked into the courtroom, single file, they assumed their positions at counsel table. The Trooper waited outside with the children, to make amends for his failure to protect them.

Her Honor admonished batterer Marty, yelled at everyone and signed the Order, in time for her nail appointment.

Marty cried the entire way down his walk of shame on the marble steps. He was evicted from the marital home; prohibited from visiting the children; and would be

*Chapter 15*
DADDY PLEASE DON'T

*After hearing the loud cracking of the glass, the girls jumped*
*out of bed. Sofia was holding her doll and Isabella had her*
*teddy bear tightly crunched in her arms. They peeked through*
*the spindles of the railing and watched with horror.*

Alex swept Alejandra off her feet at a family wedding.
She caught the bride's bouquet, and he grabbed the groom's
garter. The new couple locked eyes as the romance flourished.
Alex admired her fitted red gown with red strappy heels and
Alejandra complementing his black suit and red bowtie. He
escorted her to the dance floor for the first of many dances at
his cousin's "Black and Red" themed wedding.

It was a memory she would treasure always. They had
a whirlwind romance, marriage, and the birth of their son.
Unfortunately, the romance turned dark after their first year
of marriage. It was then his rage and verbal abuse emerged.

The bottles of liquor and beer cans filled the garbage can. Alex began drinking more after Pete was born. He abhorred the fact she had no time for him. The baby was the excuse, and he lost her attention. He remained in resentment. Apparently, he was someone who did not understand marriage or parenthood. His aggressiveness consumed him and destroyed her. He slowly tormented and ripped her apart. Her days comprised of cleaning, changing diapers and doing her best to remain sane. Alex didn't pay attention to what she had to do. He demanded her total devotion and attention. Alejandra, exhausted, barely had time to shower and take care of her own needs.

It started with verbal and emotional insults. Snide comments and demeaning remarks and calling her a stupid bitch. The more alcohol he consumed, the worst it got. Soon he started threatening to choke her or shout out "I'll kill you bitch!" Her nights were grueling, tending to the baby and fretting about her own life. She feared he would kill her and took his threats seriously. Leaving was extremely precarious. She fantasied about her escape, but every scenario involved killing him or him killing her. There didn't seem to be an option, and she chose not to tell others what was transpiring.

By their third anniversary, the abuse escalated to physical abuse. He would slap, shove, and kick her. No one, not even "alleged" friends or loved ones came to her rescue. Instead, she remained alone in the fairytale-turned-nightmare, with the evil prince lying beside her. People didn't want to get involved. She feared telling anyone what was actually happening.

Pete, now eight years old, was desperate to spend time with daddy. He would watch the abuse from behind his bedroom door, under his bed, or even in his closet. Despite daddy's brutality and the bruises he left on mommy, he craved his attention and wished to be loved.

It was a late Friday evening, and the guys were playing poker and drinking beer. All little Pete wanted was attention from his dad. He grabbed the camera, ran outside and called out "Daddy, please take a picture with me on my new camera." The guys were laughing, ignoring Pete, throwing their garbage on the patio, and focused on winning money. "Boy, you don't interrupt me on poker night. Get back in the house. Now!" Pete's face went blank, his posture fell inward, and his smile shifted to a frown. He didn't understand. Tony, Alex's friend, witnessed Pete's heartbreak and hopped out of his seat to console him. "I'll be in your picture. Let's pose. I'll put my arm around you, little man."

"Yo, that's my kid!" yelled Alex. He did not want to look like a jerk or be upstaged in front of the guys. "I'll take a picture with my little man." Pete was so happy, grinning ear to ear. Tony captured this special moment for Pete with his dad. No one saw the hell which was about to break loose coming.

Alejandra came outside, remained in the doorway, and witnessed what was taking place. She demanded Alex to stop drinking and cease his yelling and cursing in front of Pete.

Infuriated, Alex chased her into the house. "Get back inside where you belong!" They ran around the table four times. She attempted to get out of his path, but he caught her. Grabbing her forcefully, he thrust her face first into the stove. A gut wrenching scream of pain belted from the pit of her stomach. Pete witnessed it all unfold in slow motion. Frozen, he watched his mommy fall to the floor in agonizing torment. Blood dripped from her nose, down her face and onto her light blue T-shirt. Alex poured his beer all over her, as if he was pouring gasoline and ready to ignite the fire.

Pete and Tony, looking on in horror. Alex shouted, "That's what you get bitch! You don't never disrespect me in front of my friends!" Tony did nothing.

As Alex and Tony walked away, Pete rushed to his mommy and bravely said, "I'll clean you up mommy." He grabbed a bag of peas from the freezer and said, "Hold this on your nose just like on the TV commercials and I will walk you to bed." "Ok mommy?" She nodded yes, and the two slowly escaped the scene of the crime. Brave little Pete would take care of her. Alejandra barely able to walk and in shock, did not know what to do.

This episode wasn't the first, and it wasn't the last. Alex's trigger was disrespect. His machismo took over because he was too proud to let her win an argument or to let her humiliate him. Of course, he blamed her for every beating she took, as if she promoted it by merely telling him to put a fucking beer down in front of his friends.

Despite his efforts, the little man could not control his daddy, but he did what he had to in order to protect his mommy. He cared for her after the damage, by healing the wounds and hiding the black and blue with her makeup.

"You don't deserve this mommy," he comforted her. Wise for his years, he remained her protector for as long as he was able. He vowed to himself he would never to treat his wife, nor any woman like that.

Daddy never got caught and no one, friend or family member ever reported the abuse because "snitches get stitches," they all thought. As Pete grew into adulthood, he told himself, "I'll be a good father and husband someday, nothing like him".

Twenty years later, Alejandra was still being battered and abused frequently. Pete was still protecting his mother. He was now married to his beautiful Maya.

He displayed his precious photo with his daddy on the mantle. It would be a reminder of that poker night and the beating his mommy took. A devoted husband, Pete became a doting father of four-year-old Sofia and six-year-old Isabella. He remained protective of Alejandra, now known as Abuela, to the girls. It was a pleasure for her to visit her son and daughter-in-law in the suburbs. She enjoyed a hot cup of gourmet coffee with Maya for some girl chats. She cherished these times and loved her granddaughters.

One afternoon, she showed up with large, dark sunglasses, obviously to camouflage and cover some secret, a black eye or a bruise of some sort.

Maya noticed the black and blue peeking out from the bottom of Alejandra's glasses. She put her coffee mug down with one hand and slowly lifted her glasses with the other. She took a peek, and with disgust, sat back and sighed. The dark, curly-haired beauty was compassionate towards and supportive of her mother-in-law. She instantly offered her a place to stay and instructed her to grab a credit card and half of the money from the joint savings account.

"This cannot go on! Someone will get seriously hurt someday." As the ladies stared at each other, Pete returned home from work and joined the coffee clutch. He noticed his mother's sunglasses and leaned close to her to unmask the truth. With his voice escalating, he scolded her and declared, "What did he do this time, mommy!?" Pete didn't even realize how demeaning his tone was to his own mother. Had he learned this tone of voice from all he witnessed?

"You know how he is. I'll be ok, we can't change him!"

"That bastard! You must leave him, and we'll help you. Go pack your bags and sneak over here tomorrow after dad leaves for work." As she turned to leave, nodded as if to say yes, she smiled and said "OK, my little man." She knew she wouldn't leave because it was too late for her.

Maya boasted how she laid out a master plan to save her mother-in-law. She put the girls to bed and read their favorite fairytale of Prince Pete and Princess Maya. Six-year-old Isabella was in her favorite pink jammies and four-year-old Sofia was in her favorite purple jammies. They both begged to hear the story again before a good night kiss, with mommy hugging and snuggling daddy, stinking of beer.

Maya rejected his sexual advances when he had too much to drink. She remained focused on the girls. To compensate for the cold shoulder, Pete drank more and punched more, sending an unmistakable message she had no power. The fairytale of Prince Pete and Princess Maya ended when the prince started slapping, punching and kicking the princess. Despite his oath never to be like his father, he did indeed carry it forward into the next generation.

The emotional abuse and physical violence escalated, but Maya shouted back and pushed back. She was a fighter and a defender for her children. Trapped in a marriage with two babies, Maya recognized the "red flags" that her life, like Alejandra's life, was at risk, but she wasn't ready to call it abuse or to call the police.

That night, after the girls were in bed, Pete admonished Maya for offering to assist with his mother's escape from his dad. Reeking of beer, he slurred, "Bitch, you don't get in my family's business. I will choke you out!"

"Keep your voice down, the girls are sleeping!" As she started down the stairs, he ran up the stairs. He yelled, "Who are you talking to, bitch?" Without warning, he gripped her around the front of her neck with both hands and flung her over the railing, causing her to fall two flights onto the glass coffee table in the living room. The glass shattered and the blunt force of the impact crushed her skull.

After hearing the loud cracking of the glass, the girls jumped out of bed, with Sofia holding her doll and Isabella holding her teddy bear tightly. They peeked through the spindles of the railing and watched with horror as the blood leaked from Mommy's face and head, while Daddy begged for her to wake up.

Calmly, Isabella pulled out her cell phone, dialed 911 and raised the volume so the operator would hear the uncontrollable sobbing, the shouts of "I'm sorry, baby, don't die!" Maya's lifeless body, in her jammies, now stained with blood, was a horror for the children to witness. With shards of glass under her head and body, blood dripped from under her head, from her right ear and from her right nostril. She lay there, lifeless.

In shock, Pete peeked over the railing and jumped to get to her. Helpless, he sobbed uncontrollably and shouted, "I'm sorry, I'm sorry!" With snot and spit flying everywhere, he begged Maya, "Please don't die! I love you, my princess!"

Pete did not realize generational trauma got passed on. He witnessed his father assaulting his mother. He thought he coped well. Actually, it taught him reactive ways to deal with these situational incidences as an adult. At that moment, the EMTs broke down the front door and rolled in a gurney, hoping to save Maya. Pete refused to let go of her body until the police flipped him over onto the floor and handcuffed him in front of his baby girls. They read him his rights as he continued to beg Maya not to die. They dragged him out of the house and shoved him into the police cruiser. He confessed, crushed, and dismayed he could not believe what transpired. Yes, he had remorse, but it would never bring back Maya or his family.

Alejandra witnessed her baby being arrested as she pulled into the driveway. Sophia had summoned her on the cell phone, her help was needed. It was a slow motion nightmare. Alejandra watched her "little man," who had protected her for so many years, driven away in a police cruiser. His head turned back peering at his mother crying, hands cuffed. It was a nightmare, one he had when he was a little boy, fearing his own mother's death. The man in the car was his dad, not him in those nightmares.

Coupled with the sign of her lifeless daughter-in-law and angelic granddaughters was too much to bear. This was the last straw for Alejandra! Beautiful Maya had been erased from their lives. "I must take a stand for the girls."

She ran to the girls, covered their eyes, and rushed them to her minivan. Today was the day she packed for her escape from Alex. He created the monster, and he caused both fairytales to end badly, goddammit. She screamed into a pillow, not wanting the girls to hear. Alejandra stood up to Alex the night before they whisked away her little man in handcuffs. Perhaps she waited too many years. Maybe this could have been avoided if she stood up sooner? The sadness was gut wrenching torment. Her heart torn to pieces. Now she had to save the children. She couldn't save her son, and this would haunt her forever.

The EMTs were unsuccessful in saving Maya and neither could her baby girls. He murdered her by strangulation, followed by blunt trauma and sudden death, when she hit the coffee table.

The pain was unbearable. There were no words to be spoken. Only tears.

They adorned Maya with a purple blanket and purple flowers, furnished by her mother-in-law, Alejandra. She would learn of the color's symbolism and was a reminder of all the hidden acts of violence many women, children and men face daily in their homes. The pastor asked everyone to show their support to end domestic violence. The girls and Alejandra wore purple ribbons on their purple dresses. He further asked for guidance from above for everyone to understand the effects of abuse and to break the cycle in their own homes.

"We pray together for Sophia and Isabella. May they stop the cycle of violence with the help of Alejandra. We pray for Pete as he serves his life sentence in prison. May God be with him."

Frankie realized this could have been her when she heard of this event.

After both times, Dick grabbed her tiny neck and tried to squeeze the life out of her, and she was fortunate to have survived. This is Maya's story and Frankie implores everyone to be brave like Sophia and dial 911 when you witness or experience domestic violence. These stories show up in court frequently and sometimes too late.

Frankie despised her father's verbal abuse and lack of patience towards her mother. "Dad, you can't talk to mom like that!" He calmed down in his later years. He became a Grandfather to two boys and then his health deteriorated. Unfortunately, she inherited her father's lack of patience. As an attorney, she doesn't tolerate yelling from her clients or her opponents. As a mother, she refused to subject her son to it. Fortunately, he takes after his kind-hearted and calm father, which are the characteristics she longed for. With both of her men supporting and protecting her, Frankie has broken the cycle. When she grows impatient, Tom just smiles at her. When she is in the throes of arguing, her son says, "Mom, you're not being rational."

She smiles and says, "I know son, but I'm trying."

I implore all of you to be as brave as Sophia when you witness it!

Proudly wearing her purple ribbon at speaking engagements, Frankie says, "If you see something, say something".

## *Chapter 16*
Ambushed

"Yes, we have a deal, Mr. Backstabre," who represented the rapist, Frankie said, as she reassured him there would be no hearing on Monday. "Relax, Backstabre, and enjoy your weekend," she added.

Frankie drafted an Order and inspected it with her client, the Custodial Grandfather, after assuring him he didn't need to testify on Monday.

They had appeared in the courtroom, with the therapist witness, just in case anything went south. The witness had been sequestered and was required to remain in the hallway, in case there were fireworks.

As she walked in with Grandfather, she notices Backstabre at the defense counsel table with both fathers, one a meth dealer and the other a convicted rapist. "How proud you must be as you sit beside two criminals, each battling to take children away from their Grandfather in order to evade child support," Frankie thought angrily.

"Good morning Backstabre," Frankie said, as she handed him the Order to sign first. Red faced and trebling he replied, "No deal."

Shocked, Frankie answered, "What are you talking about? We had an arrangement and my client paid me attorney's fees to write the contract that YOU requested for your rapist client!"

"Yeah, but now my clients want a hearing."

"What do you mean your clients? You can't represent both of them, the dealer and the rapist, it's a conflict of interest."

"Don't care Frankie, the deal is off!" retorted Backstabre.

As His Honor took the bench and announced the case, Frankie became enraged as she was hoping to avoid putting Grandfather through more hell. He had already been through enough. She was glad to have overly prepared with witnesses ready to testify, one by phone and the other, a child psychologist, in person. And she was ready to expose the other side, especially Backstabber's client, who had beaten and raped his wife while his two-year-old was on the bed. His wife was Grandfather's daughter, who passed away after the conviction of her rapist husband to a five-year jail sentence. The two-year-old child was his precious granddaughter.

The rapist and the meth dealer presented their case first. They demanded Protective Services remove the child from Grandfather.

"Call Protective Services first." The social worker assigned to the case for Protective Services answered quickly. Questioning started. "Isn't it true the child is not safe with Maternal Grandfather?" asked Backstabre.

"No," the witness replied. "In fact, I visit the child weekly at Grandfather's house and she is safe, loved and not in any danger."

The rapist, dressed in a black suit and matching black tie, wearing nerd glasses, because he assumed a new identity in the courtroom, jumped up, approached the phone and asked, "Isn't it true you have concerns about my daughter's safety?" Frankie thought, "You had no concerns while you beat and raped your wife in front of your daughter, did you?"

"No. She is producing fine in school, and she is well-cared for."

The rapist shouted and asked the same question.

"Asked and answered, Your Honor. He is harassing the witness."

"Sustained," His Honor spoke. "Move on sir or perhaps counsel would like to resume his role as your attorney."

Frankie continued, "Unless you are too afraid of your client?"

Mr. Backstabre said, "No further questions for Protective Services."

"I call the child psychologist, Ms. Analyst."

Once she took the stand, Backstabre asked, "Isn't it true you recommended my client share custody, fifty/fifty with overnights?"

Ms. Analyst responded, "No, I never suggested that. In fact, we were working towards a transition schedule wherein he would have overnights as long as the child was ready."

"I have no further questions, Your Honor, but my client insists Ms. Analyst be dismissed as the child's therapist." "Take your ball and go home," Frankie muttered under her breath.

Frankie jumped to her feet and shouted, "Objection! There was no testimony why Ms. Analyst should be removed from this case. In fact, the father chose her through his attorney. Now, suddenly, as they are losing, the father demands his own witness be removed from the case?"

Her Honor said, "Ask your questions, Frankie." Frankie said, "Please state the schedule you are proposing for this child, Ms. Analyst."
"I recommend the child start with one overnight for thirty days and graduate during the transition stage to two overnights every other weekend."

"Ms. Analyst, I mark as Defendant's exhibit number one. Do you recognize the document entitled Agreement and Order in Custody?"

"I have not seen the document in this form, but that is precisely what I proposed during my discussions with Dad and Maternal Grandfather, who both agreed to those terms."

"As we sit here today, Ms. Analyst, what is your recommendation for Dad's visitation?"

"My recommendation is exactly the terms set forth in this proposed Order, which are the exact terms Dad and

Grandfather agreed to in my office last week. I do not know why he wants me removed and no understanding why he is asking for more time when the 7-year-old child is not ready to sleep at Dad's house, while he is still on probation. Also, he has had no counseling and is still on probation."

"Is this Order in the child's best interest?"

"Yes," she testified.

"Is Dad's proposed schedule in the child's best interest?"

"No," she replied.

"No further questions," Frankie informed the court.

Just then, Dad, the convicted rapist, jumped out of his seat again, and demanded Ms. Analyst be fired. "Remove her from the case now or I will sue her!" he shouted.

"Order in the Court!" Her Honor directed.

"Ms. Analyst, you are excused and may leave the witness stand."

"You're fired!" Dad yelled again.

"Counsel, I will write the order. Please give me a moment and please wait in the hallway. My Court Officer will hand each of you a copy when it is finished."

"Well, as least we know Ms. Analyst is not removed from the case," Frankie told her client.

The rapist stormed out of the courtroom and kicked the door. Enraged, he hollered at Backstabre, but would be no match for Frankie if he looked her way. Ready to discredit him, she thought to herself, "Get over yourself, you prick, or I'll have you arrested."

The court officer appeared with a copy for each of them. Backstabre ripped it out of her hand and stormed away, stomping down the hallway like a toddler.

In the company of Ms. Anlyst and Grandfather, Frankie reviewed the order to find the terms recommended by Ms. Anlyst were set forth in the Order. They prevailed and Grandfather was sure his daughter was there in spirit, "My granddaughter will be safe now. I hope he rots for what he did to my baby girl. He learned nothing in prison. That battering bastard tried to kill her, and she died soon thereafter because he gave her dangerous drugs".

*Chapter 17*
Honey Whispered

*"My Husband Raped Me"*

The beige walls in the courtroom lacked connection and warmth, creating an atmosphere less than welcoming. As we strolled away from day two of her custody trial, Honey broke down, sobbing uncontrollably and her body shaking after becoming overwhelmed by fear. Honey had porcelain skin, a delicate framed body and a gentle voice, invariably polite, when she asked nervously, "Can my husband rape me?"

Her husband of three years had taken custody of their baby girl, Gabriella. The same man who declared it wasn't his child. For the third time, he used her as a pawn. It was his way to attain vengeance on Honey for threatening to leave him, Guy, an attractive beef-cake lady killer. It was easy to understand why a woman was intrigued by him with such a melodic tone that could tantalize a serpent. He was the epitome of charm.

Honey met him at the office. He was a suave businessman, and he hired her as his unseasoned, innocent receptionist, his prey. They flirted in the office. It started with coy smiles, winks, and inconspicuous touches with his hand on hers when they chatted about business. Eventually, they dated after work for months. They maintained their relationship secret, but it intensified over time when his charm won her over. Honey was smitten as he enchanted her with compliments, lavish dinners, and gifts. Cautiously alluring her into his heart, he appeared to respect her as a woman and didn't force himself upon her. Honey felt secure, admired, and treated like a princess. Little did she know what was to come.

Then the kiss in his bedroom. Her eyes fixated on his, fantasizing of possibilities and a future with this Adonis. This is it! The perfect couple. Two attractive beings, respectful of each other and enthralled with each other, it seemed.

"Honey, move in with me. We can create an enchanted life together". Weak at her knees, he continued to entice her with assurances of a splendid life of luxury, love, and fulfilling her desires. Wrapping his arm around her waistline in his gentle fashion, he drew her closer. She was speechless. Sweeping her off her feet, he lifted her into his muscular arms and walked slowly into the bedroom. No words, just intense passion running through their veins, ready to consummate their relationship with delightful pleasures she never experienced. It was the first of many passionate and blissful nights for her. She never knew what to expect.

She dreamt of this perfect lifestyle and would never have achieved it on her measly salary. "I love you and I can't wait to make you mine and call you my wife," Guy promised. He groomed her to be his and was remarkably good at it. As a master manipulator and deal maker, he love-bombed her, emotionally convincing her to believe she was everything he craved. The intensity of affection he showered upon her, blinded her to what he was doing, and she lost her sovereignty, ultimately. She replied, "Yes, I would adore creating a beautiful life with you, Guy".

Her apartment was below his, so moving was easy. She sold most of her belongings, because Guy said it didn't go with his brownstone apartment design. Honey was accommodating and preferred his place, so it didn't seem to be much of an issue. She was overjoyed.

"Let's keep separate bank accounts and credit cards for a while, since I make the most money. I'll pay all the bills; you purchase the groceries. Make certain you pick up the right foods we need to maintain our beach bodies," he lectured.

It all sounded splendid and romantic to Honey. She could not contain her excitement.

So, in love, she posted new selfies of the two of them on social media without informing him. They weren't married yet, but it sure seemed like a committed relationship. She thrived in her whirlwind romance and the benefits which accompanied it: a brownstone, no bills, a handsome man, and romance every night at bedtime.

Guy surprised her with an evening of sumptuous treats, arranged just for her. He had gone home earlier than her that day, preparing his place for the next 'kill', making her desire him more. He lit candles around the living room and bedroom. Dinner for two with champagne glasses adorned the eloquent satin table setting. Fresh flowers graced the place and romantic music was playing.

As she walked in the door, the song "I'll make love to you", was playing and they were both ready for an amorous evening.

"Close your eyes, make a wish", he quietly whispered. Honey, charmed, she felt like a princess. She had never been treated this way, and Guy knew how to satisfy his woman. She made her wish. "We're going to celebrate all thru the night", were the words she heard and welcomed for this romantic interlude as they were wrapped up in each other, he captured his prey.

Dinner was served.

A soft pink glow emanated from the dining area as the gentleman pulled out her chair so his princess can be seated. She looked over her shoulder into his eyes and like a child wanting more candy. "What's next?" A smirk across his face, he did not answer. He poured her a glass of lavender champagne as she waited for his next move. He blew out one candle. The atmosphere was seductive. Tonight, was the night he would pull out all his sensual tools for his sweet Honey.

The mystery intrigued her. She anxiously awaited his next move. His hands enveloped the champagne glass, swishing the elixir around, and invited her to share from his glass. She gladly leaned into him and accepted the offer while he undressed her with his eyes, but she didn't object. He cunningly watched her every move as his adrenaline pumped in anticipation of their erotic evening, which she believed grew from love, but it actually grew from lust.

The evening was just heating up with the cuisine and the libations chosen. Guy prepared for his next move. Her intrigue heightened and her body was heating up. She waited and wondered. His cunning and devious plans swirled in his mind, but he realized he could not rush things or it would expose him as the predator he was known to prior prey. Honey did not know his past.

Always a shrewd planner and a wise business executive, he knew how to dominate every situation. She, however, was no match for him after being raised very sheltered and proper. Her sexual encounters were not as flavorful as his, but she faked it so as not to lose him. Between sips of champagne, tender kisses, a little dance or two, they proceeded through the entrée. It was time for HIS dessert.

"I don't know if I can eat any more Guy". He laughed hardily and declared, "Now it's my turn" as he swept her off her feet and whirled her around on the way to the bedroom.

Feeling very strange, lightheaded and woozy she asked him to slow down.     "Honey, it's all the excitement that has you high, you will be fine in the morning my future wife".

That's when her fairytale ended.

"Is this truly happening to me?" she asked herself. Things seemed to go perfectly for months. A dream comes true. Honey, delighted and full of excitement about their future. She woke up feeling a heaviness in her head but assumed it was from the evening of food and drinks. With no idea as to what really happened, she began her day as his future wife.

After a few brief months of living her fairytale, she was feeling nauseous, specifically in the mornings. She kept this to herself for a short time. Convinced she was pregnant, she thought, "This is it. Guy will be thrilled to be a father; he is such a warm and caring man. We will be a happy family with a son for Guy."

Euphoric, she told herself she would gift him with a son, rushing out the door to purchase a pregnancy test. " I need to hustle home, take the test", with her fingers crossed. After peeing on the stick, she nervously glanced down and observed the line slowly emerge. It was official! She was pregnant with their first child.  Without thinking she posted the announcement on Facebook as a surprise for Guy and the rest of the world. A reality check was about to shock her!

Expecting his arrival home, she set the table with candles and his favorite Chinese takeout, General Tso's Chicken, with white rice and egg roll. As she heard him open the front door, she lit the candles and expected hugs, love, and a joyous celebratory dinner.

Guy stepped into the dining room, red faced and infuriated, bellowed, "A baby?! You told the world we are expecting a baby?!! Get rid of it! I don't want a baby, never have and never will!!!! How do You know it's mine?" Shaken to the core and devastated, Honey sobbed, and whispered, "Are you calling me a whore?"

"YES, I am calling you a whore, a gold-digging whore! You set me up to have this happy little family. Only you didn't include me in the decision. GET RID OF IT!" The bitterness within this monster cast upon her heart, crushed her excitement as he stormed out of the room.

She broke down and fainted, nearly knocking the candles on the wood floor. He heard the thump. After Guy spiraled out of control, he reined himself in, blew the candles out, and carried Honey to the bedroom. Thinking to himself, he better get his crap together and play this right or something bad may come of it all.

"I'm not ready for this. If it is mine, we will get married, because I can't have my kid out there with no father. Get a paternity test before I marry you. I am not paying child support for a kid that isn't mine."

"Child support? What the hell is he talking about?" she wondered. "This is your child, and we are getting married." Tossing and turning that night, she relived the tumultuous moment of the condescending, hateful anger Guy had unleashed on his pregnant prey. "Maybe I should leave," she reflected. "I deserve better."

The next few months would be turbulent and with no affection or passion. Honey never imagined things could act so rapidly down a darkened path. Guy ignored her altogether. He became more selfish, condescending, and abusive. She overlooked the 'red flags'. There wasn't any physical abuse. Guy was too shrewd to assault a pregnant woman. Her entire world shattered, her heart crushed and a fetus growing that could bring them back together, she hoped.

The verbal abuse would escalate during her pregnancy, making Honey feel worthless, scared, and hopeless. She believed if she could provide Guy with a son, perhaps he would be happy.

While cleaning the bedroom one afternoon, she leaned down to get his dirty clothes to be laundered. A prescription bottle lay underneath his mess. Honey didn't know he was on medication. When he arrived home, she asked him if he was feeling alright while holding up the prescription bottle. He flew into a frenzy, knocked the bottle out of her hand and ordered her to never touch his stuff, ever again. Little did he realize she already investigated the prescription use and also discovered some photographs he had tucked away. She didn't say a word, for she feared for her life. Shaken to her core she needed a plan but was afraid to ask anyone for help.

Nine months sped by with tears, countless hours of praying and hoping her old Guy would return. The labor pain began with a vengeance. This baby was ready to be born. Guy was nowhere to be found and Honey had to call a cab to get to the hospital quickly. I will 'gift' him with a son, she thought as the driver rushed her to the nearby hospital.

There she was, a beautiful angel, whom she named Gabriella, after the angel Gabriel. God granted her a true angel, which made Honey smile, bring love back into her heart and a desire to live once again. Since Guy refused to acknowledge himself as the father, she did not add his name to the birth certificate.

They identified Gabriella with Honey's last name. She should have left the relationship when she had the chance.

Fearful of paying child support and fighting a custody battle, Guy gave in to Honey's wish and they got married at City Hall. No honeymoon, the romance gone, no romantic dinners. Bedtimes were now replaced with Gabriella crying, demanding mommy's attention.

Each day Guy arrived home, hungry for dinner, he was ready for a fight. His narcissistic attitude and violent tendencies escalated. As Honey felt more helpless and dependent upon him, he enjoyed it. "Now she is mine, I can do anything I want". She was miserable and did not feel safe, but realized the time had come. "I must leave to protect my precious baby girl."

I will escape while he is at work. Packing her necessities for herself and the baby, she would head back to her parents' home. There, she would feel loved, protected, and create a good life for her daughter.

Although surprised to find his home empty, he was not distraught. He was relieved to find he had his brownstone back for himself. He had to think swiftly, though. With the threat of child support looming, he filed for custody the next day. He would punish Honey for turning his life upside down. He never loved Gabby or Honey, that was her fantasy. Instead, he enjoyed watching her suffer.

At the first custody conference, Guy hired a high-powered female attorney, and Honey represented herself. After arguments and shouting over Honey, the Hearing Officer awarded shared physical custody, each parent having half of the time. Her rationale was since Gabby was a newborn, she would be in the care of grandparents during the day, while her parents worked. They were on equal footing and should share custody.

Horrified of the decision, Honey fought back, appealed the decision, and a review hearing was scheduled. Elated, Guy enjoyed every moment of facing Honey eye to eye, stealing time with the child he wanted aborted and tormenting her. His goal was to show the court she was unfit, a liar and a whore. It made no sense to Honey since he wanted nothing to do with either of them. Surely it was just his way of pretending he was better than her, so people wouldn't think less of him.

At the review hearing, again without an attorney, she approached Guy and said, "Here is your fucking paternity test. She IS yours." Gabby was eighteen months old, and Honey agonized every minute Gabby spent with her demon father. She cringed at the thought that her beautiful angel would be in the arms of this monster. Guy didn't react to the results.

As with the first hearing, there were arguments and shouting by Guy and his attorney, Ms. Spinster. The Hearing Officer affirmed her prior decision. The child, Gabby, was thriving at both households. She didn't know Guy was placing Gabby with any family member or "flavor of the week" to shift his responsibility. He wanted nothing to do with fatherhood. He was back to his old tricks, but the court didn't see any of it. It infuriated Honey. She scraped and scrounged for money to retain Frankie, as she needed a "Pitbull" to fight for Gabby and herself.

Honey never revealed the physical and sexual abuse she suffered or what she found. She denied it and distracted herself with motherhood. Honey filed the appeal herself and met with Frankie in anticipation of the trial. It was then she finally revealed Guy's domination through their short love story and turned it into a nightmare of toxic masculinity, domination, and sexual assaults.

"He called me stupid, pushed me to show how powerful he was, forced sex while I was asleep. I gave in because he was on top of me. He had drugged me."

"He drugged you?"

"Yes, more than once. Temporarily paralyzed, I lost control of my body. I found a bottle under his clothes one day. It was the same type of drug they used for date-rapes. It wasn't until I found the videos of him raping me from behind, I pieced it all together. No more romance, no love, just selfish demented acts of lust thrust upon me. I kept it secret and played the role of his dutiful wife. I still have flashbacks of those nights."

"Oh my God! Videos? You didn't deserve that."

"He told me he can take me anytime, anywhere and any way he wanted." She bowed her head in shame. Afraid anyone would find out what was happening, she could not remain silent any longer. She feared for her child. Not knowing what he would or could do to this little girl, her determination was unstoppable to save her child.

"We will expose this sick bastard," Frankie promised.

"Are you willing to reveal this or is it still too raw for you?"

"It means saving Gabby from Guy. Yes, I have to."

During the hours and months of preparation leading up to the trial, Frankie guided Honey through the stressful physical and emotional phases caused by rape. She was obviously self-loathing, blamed herself and stuffed down the rage before she uttered a word.

This incident forced Frankie to digest the rape, sickened to her stomach, she had to explain the trauma syndrome to Honey so she didn't shame herself any longer. They prepared for the next day of trial.

"Are you having any flashbacks?" asked Frankie.

"Yes, I can't sleep at night. I can't concentrate at work, or on the witness stand while that bastard stares at me. My whole life was disrupted! He has taken our baby twice and is now trying a third time to keep her from me. Doesn't any care about Gabby?"

"Yes, we care. Justice can be blind, impartial and objective. We have to present a case to show it is in the best interest of your baby girl to live with you!"

"He only wants to hurt me! It wasn't about sex; it was all about control. I was under the influence, passed out, when he flipped me over and raped me."

"He's a narcissist. It is all about the domination over you. A sick bastard!"

"My God, he's a monster, a fucking monster! She is just a defenseless child that he is using to control and humiliate me. Help me fight back, Frankie!"

After the emotionally charged hours of preparation, Frankie believed Honey was brave and strong enough to take the witness stand again. Hours of being verbally slammed by counsel and Her Honor. Honey too traumatized to reveal the abuse.

"Come forward, Ma'am and take the stand," Her Honor instructed. "Do you swear to tell the truth, the whole truth, and nothing but the truth?"

"Yes, Your Honor."

Quivering, Honey could barely answer a question. She was practically catatonic and glassy-eyed, infuriating Her Honor and Frankie's pudgy opponent. Only Frankie knew the real reason why Honey kept shrugging her shoulders and looking down at the microphone in silence. If only the system really understood abuse violations to humanity; could we better serve?

Frankie is on a mission to make this happen and bring equality to women.

Frankie was at the edge of her seat. Occasionally objecting to questions on cross-examination and wiggling in her leather seat like a child. It wasn't easy to remain quiet. Finally, her turn for re-direct arrived. Loaded with rapid-fire questions, the two rehearsed the night before.

"Why won't you communicate with your husband, Honey?"

Stoically, Honey stared at Guy, thinking to herself, "What a shitty father. He keeps winning because I won't speak of the sodomy, an inexcusable act!" Angry at herself for not speaking up earlier, she was ready to shift the stigma and the expose Guy for who is really is and how he treats women.

"Answer the question," barked her Honor.

"'I'll repeat the question, why won't you communicate with your x-husband?" Honey faced Her Honor, and in a small, shy voice whispered, "Because he raped me."

Frankie couldn't resist, "I'm sorry, I can't hear you, please repeat that, but louder."

"Because he raped me. He drugged me, and he raped me! I didn't know my husband could rape me," she blurted out angrily. "Can he rape me, Your Honor?"

Shocked, Her Honor stared through Frankie. When Frankie and Honey locked eyes ready for the next question, they shared relief that this horrific revelation released to the world, on the record, to be preserved forever.

Honey added, "He not only drugged me, sodomized me, he took photos and videos of me when I was naked and unconscious. He slipped something in my drink at a restaurant one night. I never imagined it was a drug, he said it was a 'spritzer'. My eyes began to float back into my head and I couldn't hold myself up. He told the waitress I was sick and carried me to the car. "I'm sorry ma'am she is pregnant and gets nauseous easily." "No worries, sir, I understand." I knew he was lying but did not have the ability to speak and faded off into unconsciousness.

"How did you find out what happened? Can you explain how you knew he drugged you?" inquired Frankie.

"I found pictures on his computer while I was shopping online. He saved them on the hard drive, and I found them. It was a sadistic rape, with pictures that humiliate and degrade me and I found a prescription bottle."

"Did you call the police?" Frankie asked.

"No, because I didn't know my husband could rape me." Never breaking down, numb to the interrogation, she replied, "I wake up every night, in the middle of the night, and I re-live it, like a scary movie playing over and over."

Guy jumped out of his seat and shouted, "She wanted it!"

Disgusted, Frankie quickly scribbled that on her legal pad, highlighted those words for her closing argument. Her Honor glared at Frankie and called for a recess.

Guy's pudgy lawyer was livid and said scathingly, "Yeah, sure he raped her, Frankie."

Frankie fired back, "Shame on you!"

Her Honor spoke. "Your client better get counseling fast; I want the truth from somebody before we finish this trial. We're talking about the custody of a little girl, and I need answers. Where are the police reports and why didn't she press charges?"

"We all need answers, Your Honor," replied Frankie, flushed but satisfied the rapist exposed. "Rape is the carnal knowledge of a woman by force; how does any man do that to his wife and then shout, She, wanted it?!"

She added, "Isn't justice blind, Your Honor? Only 66% of rapists are prosecuted and only 40% convicted. It's traumatizing and demeaning for all victims, and it isn't easy for her."

A date-rape doesn't always happen on a date. The attacker could be someone you know or love to make it easier for the perpetrator. Honey knew this was happening on college campuses and even to her own niece, but her?

"How could my husband rape me"?

Thoughts ran through Frankie's mind of all the incidences she had as well as friends, clients and colleagues where women are treated as the lesser. "This has got to stop", ran through her head.

"Honey will get counseling; will the rapist get any counseling?" inquired Frankie.

Red faced and furious, his attorney shouted, "Don't you dare call my client a rapist!"

"I didn't, his wife did," Frankie calmly replied.

"I'll enter a temporary Order while they both attend counseling and I want reports," Her Honor said.

"Yes, Your Honor," both attorneys responded.

Before the therapy began, and within hours of leaving the courtroom, Frankie received an Order from Her Honor that granted Honey primary physical custody and granted Guy supervised visitation through a supervisor chosen by Honey. She selected her police officer brother, Mac, to supervise the rapist, and now had to reveal the rape to Mac so he could protect Gabby. It was worth the humiliation of sharing the tape with Mac, even though Mac could have taken legal action to protect Honey years ago.

Frankie researched Guy's criminal history to discover charges were pending for sexually assaulting his new secretary. All the trial dates were cancelled so he could face his accuser at the rape trial. They called Honey to testify as the star witness for the prosecution, and now she was strong enough to stare him down and make him squirm the way he made her squirm in the custody battle. She was strong enough to relive her own rape, although the trauma never left her. She found the strength to protect Gabby, and she became a warrior for Guy's other victims and for herself.

Honey remained in the courtroom after her testimony and found a seat in the gallery to watch Guy identified as a serial rapist. Everyone witnessed his guilty plea for raping the unsuspecting new secretary. Honey wished that she had spoken up sooner, but couldn't blame herself for his heinous acts against women. That was his crime and will pay for it as a registered sex offender and as a father unable to have Gabby without supervision.

Frankie takes her role as protector and warrior as the most important thing in all her cases. She extends the lifeline to every client, and sadly, not every client grabs it. Honey had lifelines through her brother Mac and other family members, but she didn't grab them. As with Frankie, she saw the 'red flags' and ignored them. Fortunately, in this case, justice prevailed for little Gabby, and she will always be safe with her mommy.

During therapy, Honey would relive the trauma, address her self-loathing and attempt to heal. She would do it for Gabby.

*Empowered Frankie*

*Chapter 18*
Revelations in The Boardroom

*Frankie was always one choice away from changing her future. At times she made her own choices. However, at transformative times, the choices were made for her.*

On a snowy winter morning, Frankie had a forty-minute drive to the country club for the annual board meeting for her favorite charity.

Always wanting her parents' praise and acceptance, Frankie lived with this feeling no matter how much she achieved, it was never enough. As a woman, she typically felt she was treated as the lesser sex. Today, however, things were going to change. Finally, she sat at the mahogany boardroom table with many affluent businessmen. Often it was a challenge to accept her position, because she truly did not believe in herself enough. Who am I to assume I could sit amongst lawyers, judges and affluent professionals? A revelation was coming!

A silvery-haired male attorney paid her no regard, denied she was even present. Reflecting upon her years at the family dinner table, her presence was often negated and ignored, and her voice hushed. This would be different, she knew. Frankie differed from her fellow representatives in many aspects and defined herself as: Female attorney, survivor and warrior against domestic violence and fundraiser. No one here has my story; she could tell as she glanced around the room, filled with a majority of men. There will be an appropriate moment to wake them up out of their ignorance. She thought to herself, they seemed to be impressed with status versus purpose. Ok, I can play their game. My Coach purse and the beautiful diamonds Tom has showered me with will certainly help me blend in.

Frankie earned her position as a Board Member in the fight against domestic violence with unrelenting drive, soliciting for donations and making donations herself during her six years of service. They did not accept her to the boardroom because of her stellar performance in the courtroom. She won it as a fierce warrior against domestic violence.

At the beginning, she maintained her "secret" and patiently examined the inner workings of the organization. She listened to the silver-haired gentlemen steal the limelight, dominate the women, and neglect the "on the ground needs" of victims. Sure, they had to concentrate on liability insurance, local government funding, state government grants, therapeutic services, legal representation and housing, but "I need to fight, and I know how," she reminded herself.

So many times, she squirmed in her chair as they pontificated. Not known to be a patient person, Frankie advised herself to *"Sharpen your tools and pull them out at the appropriate time. Just nod while they pat themselves on the back,"* she strategized. *"Maybe if they have stood in my heels or the shoes of our victims and the brave survivors,"* or *"observed it in the home as children,"* or *"perhaps saw their own mother survive it,"* she surmised. No matter the reason, these successful board members are here socializing in the aroma of gourmet coffee. It's not time to reveal my story; today is not the day, keep it secret Frankie."

As the chef sauteed the spinach, peppers and onions for the omelets and the whiff of bacon infused the room, the Board members were summoned to partake in the continental breakfast buffet. It was an array of luscious pastries, fresh fruit, toast and jam or bagels with cream cheese. Frankie took her place in the buffet line and requested her egg-white and spinach omelet the way she preferred, just like she made at home. Clearly, she couldn't say no to the bacon or the fresh fruit medley. The scent of that decadent brunch in the tearoom of the opulent country club welcomed Frankie to her new lifestyle, but she never forgot her old life.

Frankie delighted in her perfectly prepared personal omelet with hand-picked side dishes. Enjoying a bowl of fresh tropical fruit, she savored her gourmet coffee served in china cups, accompanied by more chatting with members seated at her table. They discussed Frankie's plans for the next fundraiser and conducted small talk about their families and the special treatment offered them on this winter morning. As a bell sounded, they were ushered into the boardroom, where pastry, chocolate mints, herbal tea, iced tea and more coffee awaited their arrival. Frankie prepared an iced coffee for herself and grabbed a few mints for refreshment.

At each place, the agenda set in a leather-bound folder, beside pens and notepads, the meeting was "called to order." A blazing flame roared in the fireplace. She gazed out the window at the crystal snowflakes falling before her eyes. "This is surreal," she reflected. "How do I enjoy this experience in a comfy cashmere sweater, sitting in an oversized leather chair, knowing victims and children are living in a shelter?" she anguished. "Sip your coffee, Frankie," she told herself. "To empower them and yourself, observe and learn, don't share your secret, yet."

How many of them devoted their time and passion to fund raising, spending countless hours begging colleagues for donations for a greater cause, she wondered. Frankie recalled the diligent hours and painful revelations of her own tragedy, all hidden within her briefcase. For ten years and hundreds of thousands of dollars, she paid it forward, helping other warriors fighting to survive. All this luxury and pampering was uncomfortable, yet it made sense why she was being shown this lifestyle. It created a separation, a safety net.

For the first time in her adult life, motherhood, court hearings, the fight for equality, the fight against sexism, the fight against sexual assault, family crises, or family funerals, did not distract her. "Today," she understood. "I am being rewarded for thirty years of survival followed by thriving as a powerful attorney, an influential advocate and a warrior against domestic violence." The cashmere sweater, endless buffet, indulging that morning and her seat at the Board Table were rewards she earned.

*Remaining silent while processing every word said at these meetings for five years, she asked herself, "How do I engage with the silver-haired gentlemen, surrounding me, who know nothing about being strangled or dragged by the hair or stabbed, or punched in the face or raped?"* Just then, one of the grey-haired attorneys, Edward said offhandedly, "We have too many attorneys on this board and some need to go." Alarmed, Frankie, did not react outwardly. With eyes wide-opened, insulted, the kind-hearted Director, Rosie, folded her arms and threw herself back in her chair. "Really, Edward," she replied serenely, "Let's take a poll and find out why each of us serves on the board."

Frankie gulped and contemplated, "This is the moment to reveal my secret." Wringing her hands in great distress, powerless to change the situation she now encountered, "What do I suggest? Do I take that pompous ass down? Do I keep my secret? That rich old man, how dare he? Was he ever strangled?"

There was an icy cold tension in the air. Colleagues would have to deny someone the opportunity just because 'he' didn't like the legal representation. Why? What is he hiding? Frankie wondered.

Minutes seemed like hours as each member responded, although she heard nothing come out of their mouths because something trapped her in her dreams, in her struggle to bring Edward down or to expose her secret.

It was her turn. She was confronted. "Why are you a member, Frankie?" This was the moment after thirty years of secrets she never wanted to face! It didn't matter now how much fear she had. She knew her voice was needed. Resentfully, she stared at Edward and declared, "I am a survivor!"

The entire room went silent. Edward sat there, face blank and said nothing. "Don't put your head down, girl! Stare at him until he puts his down." Frankie told herself. Out of nowhere, another female Board Member, sitting next to Frankie added, "I am a Board Member because I too am a survivor!" Frankie was stunned and happy at the same time. This is what we need, the 'real voices' speaking up.

The silence was deafening. Now, Rosie grinned as Edward was put in his place and he slid down into his chair.

Thirty years of silence; of hiding and now in front of all these people, her secret was out. She couldn't handle it. Frankie rushed to the restroom to hide or cry or celebrate. Someone entered and she turned to see Liz, who had followed her. Acknowledging each other face to face, teary-eyed, they comforted each other. Liz said to her "You didn't deserve that." These two warriors served as Board members for several years and had carried their ugly secrets until that moment on a snowy morning, side-by-side at the Board Table. They each took a deep breath, smiled at each other, and went right back to the boardroom to discuss finances and housing for survivors. After shutting down Edward, he remained quiet the remainder of the meeting. What would come of all of this?

Frankie left the meeting and drove home feeling accomplished. She had the taste of coffee on her breath, accompanied by a taste of power because she was empowered by inspiring others. She had freed herself from the fear of shame.

This was only the beginning of her mission and purpose. Her unstoppable nature aligned her with organizations, speaking engagements. Writing her book to help others stand up for their rights, to live their dream and fulfilled lives. Not battered, not beaten, for they had enough of the slaps, the tears, the bruises and the outbursts damaging relationships.

Frankie realized her entire life revealed her path. The plan was always to be there to fight the fight no one else would. Silvery haired man didn't scare her. He would not break her legs, and no one was shoving a meatball down her throat to shut her up, ever again.

She earned her seat at the head of the boardroom table at her law firm, where she stands in her power in order to empower others.

Many years later, Frankie would look back at her own story and awaken to many insights. She would heal beyond her imagination because she told her story.

## *Chapter 19*
### After the Trauma

Over the years, Frankie attended several conferences organized for local judges and attorneys of all ages and areas of the law to mingle, learn, or teach each other. The one seminar Frankie desperately needed to attend was entitled "After the Trauma." With trepidation, she signed up, nervous she would learn something about her trauma and excited she would learn more about her clients' trauma. As always, she put her clients first.

She walked in slowly, glancing around the room to see if any of her colleagues would see through her. She hoped not be exposed as a victim, rather be seen as Frankie, focusing on sharpening her skills for the courtroom.

As she set up her legal pad and checked several emails, the program begun with an all-female panel. Faced with a Power Point presentation indicating medical proof that trauma causes changes in the brain. "Oh no, what changes am I facing?" she thought. She nervously took notes and feverishly wrote, "during a traumatic event, the brain takes control and shifts the body into reactive mode. Shutting down all other processes, the brain goes into survival mode, allowing the brain to shift back to the normal structure of control, so the brain and the body react and change. However, understanding the changes is the tough part. When the immediate threat is over, stress is reduced, and the brain can shift back to normal."

Clearly, my clients will never understand this nor acknowledge it. "We all heal differently," she told everyone, including herself. For thirty years, she rejected the notion she was damaged or broken. "I didn't have a black eye," Young Frankie thought as she overlooked the abuse because it helped her cope and focus on how to survive. She worked hard, and she put her husband, child, family, work and her clients first. Her denial provided her the strength to adjust to the shock and pain for over thirty years until she was ready to face and share it. Basically, like a majority of victims, she denied it for fear of shame. She took the hits and didn't fight back to avoid the shame.

"I successfully conquered it and shared my skills with others," she thought. She took a deep breath and hoped she was not permanently affected by the strangulation and the punch to the head. Overwhelmed by the terror and the pain, Young Frankie had no resources to cope with her own trauma. However, Attorney Frankie haphazardly had collected the resources needed to fight for others, because no one offered them freely.

Twenty-five years of struggling for respect and acknowledgement within the legal profession came to an end after being enlightened at the seminar. Sitting alone in the dining room, sipping a steamy and frothy cappuccino that September morning at Camelback Mountain, Her Honor quietly approached Frankie and sat directly across from her. She asked about how domestic violence was being dealt with in the court system and her personal quest to recognize trauma and the victims' reaction and/or inaction. When asked why they didn't fight back, Frankie responded, "We all heal differently, Your Honor." Eyebrow raised, she added, "I just don't understand it."

No longer ashamed of her secret, and feeling stronger in her self-belief, it was Frankie's turn to ask the questions, "Can you see the truth from the bench?" was her first question. "Yes," replied Her Honor, "There is almost always one comment or gesture I can see from the bench that helps me see the truth, so I can render my decision." Just then, a second judge joined them, and Frankie greeted her, "Good morning, Your Honor, we are discussing the presentation, as well as the violence and the trauma we see every week." Frankie asked her, "Can you see the truth from the bench, Your Honor?" "Yes, I do," she said, "It takes time and thorough questioning, but the truth reveals itself through testimony." With fifty years of combined experience between the two judges, it offered some hope for Frankie that judges seek to make the right decision, although she reminded them the victim will only reveal the truth when the victim is ready because the system is erroneously designed to re-victimize him/her.

As she looked to her left, a third judge joined them, three female judges in a semi-circle with Frankie. Before the conversation could continue, His Honor pulled up a chair to the left of Frankie, and he joined the conversation with no trepidation. Within minutes, eight judges had joined Frankie, all wanting more information on domestic violence. For the first time, Frankie had those on the bench to herself. Speechless for a moment, she looked from left to right to scan the full circle. Stunned, Frankie inquired, "Am I in heaven, surrounded by all of you?" One female judge said, "This sure isn't heaven."

The scent of fresh baked goods permeated the room. Homemade raisin-filled scones, jumbo chocolate chip cookies, and a fresh fruit medley were being offered with herbal tea and hot coffee, and the circle of distinguished jurists disbursed. Frankie left first, and the others headed in different directions. Frankie processed the events that had unfolded, events she could never have expected during her twenty-five-year journey. "Don't question it, revel in it," she thought.

It was a moment Frankie would never forget, undeniable and irrefutable proof she was respected by and invited to sit among the judges, the "Triers of Fact," whom she stands before every day in the pursuit of justice. As she headed to the Adirondack chairs with her scone to face the Indian Summer sun, she reminded herself she was a warrior against domestic violence. In her "mom life" t-shirt and jeans, she was reminded of all she overcame and conquered in order to sit in that chair with a sweet treat in this cherished moment.

## *Chapter 20*
## He's Coming to Kill You

*"Frankie!" squealed her raspy voiced secretary. "He's coming to kill you!"*

He despised Frankie because she exposed him for the abusive, vicious bastard of a spouse and father he was. Her secret was similar to many of the individuals dealing with domestic violence. This one would not get away with his cruelty. Petite Sissy and her child were brutally persecuted for years before she reached out for advice. She's fortunate to be alive. I can't express the same for Whitefox.

6 months prior, Sonny Shine, a colleague of Frankie's, phoned in a panic. "I require your help. If you don't help, I may require bail money for killing him."

"What are you talking about, Sonny?"

"You recall that fellow, Whitefox? Sissy's husband, you saw in court last month?" "Yeah."

"Well, the bastard found my address, popped up at my house. He pounded on the door demanding to see me."

"No way!"

"Way. My daughter rushed out of the shower with her bathrobe on and holding a bar of soap. When she opened the door, she came face to face with that messed up, sick, smelly bastard."

"Oh no! Is she okay?"

"Thank God yes. He was screaming at her for me to come to the door. He ferociously demanded to see me and said a few other choice things. When she told him she was calling the police, he left. I cannot imagine what I would have done if he had hurt her."

Scaredy-cat Whitefox may have run away, but the damage was done. He clearly found Sonny's family. The encounter with his daughter could have been a nightmare. Enraged and distressed, he had to protect his family and himself.

"You're the toughest, no bullshit lawyer I know. I need you to take down that beast, save Sissy and keep me out of jail."

"When is the hearing?"

"Two days from today. I'll bring you the files now. You gotta help me, please!"

Knowing what it was like to live through these nightmares, Frankie agreed to help, especially for the safety of Sissy and her child. She felt the resentment she had stuffed down for years bubbling up like a volcano.

Later in the day, a good-looking Italian attorney entered her office, wearing a grey pinstriped suit. He embraced Frankie, deposited the files, and ran out of her office. It was an intense moment, and she could sense and feel his fear. So intense it coursed through her veins. It was obvious how tormented and desperate he was and needed support. Frankie pondered, now understanding his predicament. As an advocate who understood the system, she knew resources, and was compelled to support those who required it.

*If only I had known what I know now for myself....*

The bloody photos of Sissy made her sick to her stomach as she coordinated the evidence for the hearing. Dear God, she reminisced, this could have been me.

"Explosive Disorder?"

The court appointed therapist revealed Whitefox's diagnosis. Apparently, he exhibited multiple unwarranted episodes of anger and flying into rage for no reason. She subpoenaed the therapist to testify even though it was evident in the files. He, too, feared Whitefox. Why do these fits of rage overcome people? She wondered. It is very similar to Dick. This haunted her to put an end to it. She wanted and needed to understand for her own healing as well. Perhaps, like Dick who felt abandoned, others go through this tremendous pain never knowing how to process their grief and loss.

Reviewing the evidence, investigating every piece, analyzing it diligently, Frankie was ready. She was determined to put Whitefox to rest, no longer able to hurt anyone or himself. She slept little during this time, as she found herself reliving her own personal hell. Her heart ached for Sissy and for herself.

On the way to the courthouse, Frankie stopped at the sheriff's office. She requested an escort for Sissy. Buddy, one of the beefiest no-nonsense sheriffs, appeared. A quick briefing about the threat of violence and how to handle the situation should it arise made Frankie relax... a little. She had trepidation but hid it well.

"I have to be strong for Sissy." She realized it was for herself, too. If she should any signs of her own trauma, they would dismiss her from the case. "Why did I become an attorney?" she asked herself once more.

Buddy escorted both ladies to the counsel table. Whitefox sat at his table, without counsel, in filthy jeans and an unwashed T-shirt. It wasn't anything like a TV law show where they show up in a suit, looking entirely different. This was raw! He wasn't the least bit embarrassed by his messy grey hair, greasy fingernails or the stench of body odor.

Sissy trembled, hardly able to utter a word. She was glued to Frankie's side. Petite Frankie was not about to take any shit. She body-blocked Whitefox so he couldn't look past her or intimidate Sissy. Loudly and contemptuously, she spoke and presented the evidence of Sissy's bloody face.

"Don't lose your cool girl," she murmured in her head.

Buddy continued to provide protection, as Frankie cited Whitefox until he lost control. He shouted, spit and lunged at her from across his table every time she got within inches of him. "If only I could lock his ass up now." Buddy grabbed his shoulders and sat him down like a toddler in the throes of a tantrum. Frankie refrained from any smug remarks or sneers.

"Do you swear to tell the truth the whole truth...?" Sissy responded, "Yes. He locked my six-year-old son in the trunk of his car during visitation. His excuse was because he said, 'Daddy, I hate you!'" Savagely, Whitefox lunged at Frankie again. "Order in the court," Her Honor demanded, pounding the gavel. Buddy pushed him back down in his seat, with a little more umph than previously.

Frankie was fearless and determined. This shit would no longer abuse a child or his spouse. "Your Honor, here are the Protection Order against Whitefox." She presented the copies.

Lunging one more time across the table, Buddy manhandled him. "I've seen and heard enough counsel. There is no need for the therapist to testify. Mr. Whitefox, I am suspending all of your custodial time. It is unclear why you are not in jail, given the danger you pose to all of us," exclaimed Her Honor.

Humiliated, he wanted Frankie dead. The rage in his eyes was evident to everybody in the court.

Ms. Raspy, the receptionist with her cigarette dangling out of her mouth, relayed the death threat to Frankie, shaken and visibly concerned. Unnerved by the warning, infuriated, Frankie kicked off her heels, hiked up her skirt and hauled herself down the alley, straight to the police station to press charges. That shit will not get away with this, and I'm not remaining silent. I'll show him. Barging through the glass doors, the entire force turned their eyes and felt her fury. She spotted a young female police officer. Careful not to fall over, she shoved her heels back on, caught her breath and proclaimed, "I'm an attorney from Barrister Lane and I must see Chief Champion NOW!"

"Ok, ok" replied the brand-new Lieutenant Copper. "Calm down and have a seat ma'am." "Calm down? He threatened to kill me!" The tiny brunette wearing a slicked back bun rushed down the hallway and barged into the chief's office. "Cool, a female officer, she'll understand." Frankie thought.

Ready to present the facts and prepared with Whitefox's criminal record, she refused to assume the role of victim. Fueled by her anger and secrets, she anxiously waited to be saved. Frankie demanded justice for herself.

She was hit with the sudden revelation she too deserved protection. She had fought so many battles for others, hiding her own suffering. For the first time, Fearless Frankie emerged, not for others but for herself. There was no reason to protect this criminal. He deserved punishment to the fullest extent of the law, and she, like those she protected, deserved justice and peace.

Lieutenant Copper escorted Chief Champion through the corridor and introduced him to Frankie.

"No tears, just facts," Frankie instructed herself. The Lieutenant winked at Frankie and returned to her position at the front desk, eavesdropping on this alarming sequence of events. Frankie commanded the Chief's attention. Fear turned to rage as the victim transformed into the advocate. She pointed to Whitefox's history and directed him through the history of simple assault, aggravated assault, harassment of five women, three of whom were his ex-wives.

In her formal lawyer manner, she recounted the harassment in the courtroom the day prior. "Chief, Whitefox repeatedly went to grab me while sitting at the defendant's table. He was screaming, 'You bitch!'"

Frankie presented her copy of the Protection Orders to the Chief and informed him Whitefox's physical and legal custody was suspended. Ringing in her owns ears, she heard the little boy screaming "Daddy, I hate you," reminding her of the times she felt the same way towards her abuser, Dick. Her fire was up, and no one was going to stop her now.

"We know about Whitefox. He is notorious for stalking and harassment. I can't believe he is still alive," he said. "Yes, and this time he tried to kill his son!" she announced furiously. "How can a father lock their own child in a trunk for nine minutes? He could have suffocated!"

Enraged, attempting to not lose control over her emotions, Frankie continued. "He assaulted all three of his wives. Now his abuse has escalated. He attempted to murder his son. Sissy frightened, never reported it, so he wasn't charged. If she had, he would have lost custody sooner," she opined. Flashbacks of her own secrets gave her more reason to pursue justice. How many of us don't tell, ran through her head?

The Chief shook his head while she continued. "I had to ignore his violent outbursts so I could present my case, on behalf of Sissy and her child. Her Honor remained stoic, listening to the facts, and witnessed what unfolded before her eyes before rendering her decision. Sissy is fearful of retaliation because only a piece of paper protects her from this monster. Moreover, I sit here wondering if he will ambush me as I walk down the alley."

"Get me a description of his vehicle." The chief said forcefully.

Prepared, she stated, "Here is the description of his tow truck and car. If he shows up at my office, I need protection. I want him charged!" she declared, admittedly.

The chief took the allegations seriously. He wanted him off the streets, just as bad as Frankie did. He would charge Whitefox with terroristic threats, defined in the Crimes Code as "causing reasonable expectation or fear of imminent bodily injury, a crime of violence with intent to terrorize another." In addition, charges of harassment, any threat of a strike, shove, kick or otherwise subjects another to physical contact or attempt to or threaten to do the same, could be added.

Holy crap, she thought, taking a deep centering breath, this was everything Frankie could have charged her abuser and put Dick in jail. If only she knew then, there were laws to protect her. Then there is the issue of shame and denial. She needed a Frankie to be her advocate back in those days.

This is a momentous transformation, she realized. She extended her shaking hand to the Chief and thanked him for acknowledging the crimes Whitefox committed. They were real and dangerous. Confident the Chief would be watching, she felt safer.

Upon her return to the office, she decided to leave the scene and drive home.

"Tom, I did it! I stood up for Sissy and myself." Tom congratulated her on the phone, cheered her on, and would wait for her when she arrived home.

Flashbacks floated through her head. This time, she did not keep a secret and found the courage to charge her abuser. The strength she now had was helping others, too. Maybe Frankie needed to defend and protect someone else, like she did in her younger days. Maybe that was her lesson. To be strong for another, I found my power; she realized. Just like Sissy stepped up to save her son. That was her driving force.

*Now, I'm a protector.*

She jumped out of the car and ran to Tom, who was standing in the driveway to embrace his sweetie as she relaxed her body into his chest and took a deep sigh, a tear rolling down her cheek. "They are going to charge him with terroristic threats."

"No worries honey, I already called the alarm company, and I am armed." Even though his words were reassuring, Frankie was still going to carry mace in her purse and keep a paring knife in her desk drawer.
It felt like an immense weight had finally released, even though this was not over yet.

With Tom by her side, Frankie felt safe. He took her hand as they walked together into the house. Dinner was already prepared. Two glasses of wine, staring into each other's eyes, they toasted to a life of freedom from the shackles of her mind and heart.

Five foot two, Frankie would face him at his criminal jury trial. She would be brave enough to fight back. Three times at the Magisterial court and then twice before his Honor. Three times she survived Dick's attempts to kill her. No way was she quitting now.

Whitefox forced Ms. Raspy and Frankie to testify, contending the District Attorney did not have enough evidence to prove he committed a crime. The Magistrate ruled against him. The courtroom was heated. Tension crackled like lightening in the air. Frankie controlled the tapping of her pen on the desk, she could not stop playing the memories over in her mind.

Whitefox filed a Motion to Dismiss, claiming the Magistrate had incorrectly allowed the case to move forward and wanted the charges dropped. "He's got to be kidding!" Frankie wanted to scream it out loud in the courtroom. Gritting her teeth, she wanted to hit him in the head with her files.

It was getting more challenging to control her emotions. They were pent up for years. All eyes switching back and forth, anxiously waiting to hear what His Honor would say. Frankie felt everything all over again, reliving her trauma from the past and real time.

"The petition is dismissed, and this case will be scheduled for trial. Court adjourned."

OMG. Frankie turned towards Tom, wanting to scream, "We did it!" She knew well enough it wasn't over yet. With the law on her side, she had a weapon that armed her. If only I could have looked at Dick, the same way I stared down Whitefox.

On the way back to her office, she would cross paths with Ima Traitor, Esq, Whitefox's attorney. "I'm sorry about what happened, I'm just doing my job," winking at Frankie. "So was I. You won't win this. You are representing a serial abuser who threatened to kill your colleague." Infuriated, her eyes flared wide open, "You can go to hell!"

How does someone sleep knowing this? Some people will do anything for money. I should know this when I think back to all the dope Dick sold to make money. Where is one's integrity? So many thoughts flowed through her head on the drive home.

A disturbing night of upsetting dreams, flashbacks, and possible outcomes.

"Get up babe, you are going to be late."

"Oh Shit!" Frankie shook off her nerves the best she could, put her plum suit and black heels on and off she went for the trial.

Tom took her hand, a pillar of strength, and walked to the Halls of Justice. A gentleman always, he held open the big glass door for his rock, although she never realized it. Tom had his jaunt with failing relationships and women who couldn't make decisions. He appreciated Frankie's directness, respected she knew what she wanted, and loved her sense of humor. They stood in line at the security checkpoint, sat together on the uncomfortable bench while he prayed she would finally release her past and get justice.

A parade of colleagues entered the courtroom. Each stopping by to make 'small talk,' providing some extra support for her. Frankie became more confident because this was her turf and she felt safer.

Buddy suddenly appears out of nowhere. Equally shocked to see her, he said "What the hell are you doing here?"

"It's round two with that bastard," she whispered. "It's not a custody hearing; he threatened to kill me!"

Buddy placed his hand on Tom's shoulder, slightly tapping and reassuring him. "Whitefox tormented your wife that day. He needs to pay for this!" Tom nodded. He knew better than to say anything that may upset Frankie further. He hurried away to courtroom A, where he, ironically, was assigned to the Whitefox trial.

Peering out the door, scanning the room, he knew

this was a tense situation. I can't wait to watch this trial, he thought. He assumed his position behind Whitefox, who was already unnerved. You could almost hear his heart thump, his blood pressure soar and the revenge and hatred spewing through his sweat.

Every footstep on the tile floors echoed in the chamber. Whispers got louder, Frankie holding her ground and hoping she didn't lose it. It was all too much to handle after 30 years of secrets and now standing up for her life. The clock kept ticking and tension was building.

What if the jury doesn't like me? What if they think I'm an overly confident attorney?

Calming her own thoughts, she assured herself they would Hate him. What is taking them so long? It's been three hours while they did the jury selection. Frankie was becoming impatient. What if I just drop the case and walk away? No! I've come too far, and I must do this. It's my purpose to stand for justice. The symbol of lady justice reminded her she stood for the morality of the justice system, and she would prove it works. No more hiding.

The disheveled and disinterested Assistant District of Attorney, Slipshod, approached them and instructed the two of them to get some lunch. "We should be ready to proceed soon."

They barely made it back to Frankie's office when they were summoned back to Courtroom A. An urgent message came from Mrs. Raspy. "Whitefox wants to make a deal. Get back here now you two!"

Frankie glared at Tom, who knew her fire was explosive, placed his hands on her back and guided her back to the conference room. She didn't say a word. That couldn't be good.

"He wants to plead guilty to disorderly conduct," Slipshod reported. A summary offense with only a small fine of three hundred dollars. "What do you think, Frankie?"

"Bullshit!" Now standing strong in her role as an attorney, she barked: "He pleads guilty to harassment with a huge fine or we go to trial. I want a paper trail of this shit, so any woman or child he threatens can use this guilty plea to prove his pattern of abusive and criminal conduct."

Silence. Dead silence until she continued. "At the very least, I can lay the groundwork for those who cannot fight for themselves and store these secrets for a lifetime, terrified to tell."

Slipshod knew she was right. "I get it. I'll see if I can sell it. Sit tight!"

Pacing the floor, waiting, Fearless Frankie served Young Frankie. She pulled her out of the ashes and rubble from the trauma that paralyzed her with fear and the inability to stand up for herself and fight. Everyone was quiet.

Whitefox reluctantly took the deal. Buddy was breathing down his back like a salivating dog, staring him down with an intimating attitude. Frankie, ready to testify and holding strong and His Honor ready to shame him.

Soon it would be over, she hoped.

Forced to face this derelict who smelled like an old garbage can, a dirty old man; she stood with an inner power saying under her breath, "You will not make me cry!" Buddy and Tom were her bodyguards. Walking to her seat mumbling softly, "I'm not afraid to look at you. Sissy and I survived your attempt to break us!" Shaking inside, she would allow no one to see her vulnerabilities, especially Whitefox.

Everyone waited. The silence was deafening.

The gavel came cracking down like a bolt of lightning and his Honor shouted, "Order in the Court".

Everyone sat at attention while the grey haired, nearly retired, wrinkly old judge admonished Whitefox for his threats. He shamed his unconscionable behavior towards an Office of the Court, squinting with a determined look of revenge.

"Frankie, is the guilty plea satisfactory to you?"

"Yes, Your Honor, the plea is acceptable to me." She really wanted to say, "Fuck yeah" and jump up to give him a high five.

Frankie sat down, doing her best not to gloat over his fate, but it sure felt good.

"Please stand Mr. Whitefox." He trembled, rubbing his hands together, sobbing like a coward as he looked down at his dirty sneakers.

They all fucking sob!

Scribbled on her notepad, her last words. "Screw Whitefox, it's over!"

*He walked away, crying.*

## *EPILOGUE*

*It is uncanny how Frankie was led to be an attorney protecting those who also experienced brutal violence like she had. It made her a better lawyer, no doubt.*

Kathy was often asked why she didn't seek help or leave. Victims of domestic violence rarely seek assistance as a result of fear, self-preservation, and hopelessness. She finally saw the signs and was ready to accept the gifts offered to her by strangers and friends, traveling a long road full of roadblocks.

Thirty years later, Kathy understood those signs were sent so she could succeed and pay it forward to others.

*"Don't ignore the signs, accept help from others."*

There are means of escape all around you, bartenders will help if you need to escape from a bar, emergency room physicians will help if medical care is needed, and there are many organizations that fight against domestic violence and sexual assault. Google it and call the hotline!

Be sure to check out your local resources and the resources listed at the end of this book to help victims of sexual abuse and domestic violence.

If you see something, say something and say *No More to domestic violence.*

Kathy Piperno, Esq. is a survivor who kept a secret for thirty years. These stories are representative of the lives and situations many have gone through. All the names and situations have been fictionalized to protect innocent people. Kathy is now fearless and walks in her power to defend those victimized and to create a better system for all. Her hope is that these scenarios have touched you deeply, enough to help another, to speak up and to listen.

*Resources*

NATIONAL COALITION AGAINST DOMESTIC
VIOLENCE
Denver, Co. (303)839-1852

PENNSYLVANIA COALITION AGAINST
DOMESSTIC VIOLENCE
National Helpline 1(800)99-SAFE (7233)

NATIONAL DOMESTIC VIOLENCE HOTLINE
(800)799-7233

DELAWARE COUNTY VICTIM ASSISTANCE,
Media, PA
24-Hour Sexual Assault Victim Hotline (610)566-4342
Crime Victims Law Project (610)-566-6463

DOMESTIC ABUSE PROJECT of DELAWARE
COUNTY, Media, PA
24-Hour Hotline: (610)565-6272

WOMEN AGAINST ABUSE, Phila., Pa. (215)386-1280

HUMAN TRAFFICKING HELP HOTLINE:
(800)654-1211

DOMESTIC SHELTERS.ORG.

NYC 24-hour hotline (800)621-HOPE

"e-Body Guard" APP -notifies 911 (888)819-7636

"VictimsVoice" Web App: (609)435-3551

https://www.psychologytoday.com

https://www.psychologytools.com

https://www.thehotline.org

https://ncadv.org

https://www.mayoclinic.org

# POWER AND CONTROL WHEEL

Physical and sexual assaults, or threats to commit them, are the most apparent forms of domestic violence and are usually the actions that allow others to become aware of the problem. However, regular use of other abusive behaviors by the batterer, when reinforced by one or more acts of physical violence, make up a larger system of abuse. Although physical assaults may occur only once or occasionally, they instill threat of future violent attacks and allow the abuser to take control of the woman's life and circumstances.

The Power & Control diagram is a particularly helpful tool in understanding the overall pattern of abusive and violent behaviors, which are used by a batterer to establish and maintain control over his partner. Very often, one or more violent incidents are accompanied by an array of these other types of abuse. They are less easily identified, yet firmly establish a pattern of intimidation and control in the relationship.

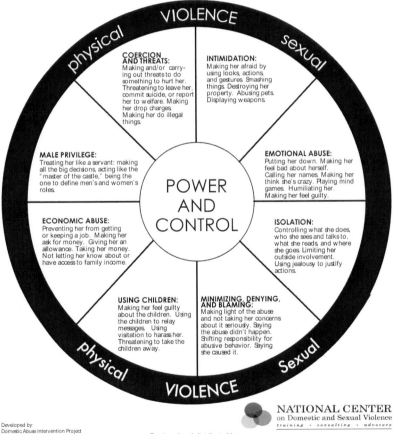

NATIONAL CENTER
on Domestic and Sexual Violence
*training • consulting • advocacy*

Developed by:
Domestic Abuse Intervention Project
202 East Superior Street
Duluth, MN 55802
218.722.4134

Produced and distributed by:

## *About Kathy*

Kathleen Piperno is a Partner with Eckell Sparks, the first female partner in the Family Law Division. She practices exclusively in Family Law including child support, custody, divorce, equitable distribution, protection from abuse, termination of parental rights and adoption.

As a survivor herself, she has devoted her career to the fight against domestic violence. Kathy's volunteer efforts include volunteer for Women Against Abuse; consultant for the School of Social Work at Neumann University; Board Member of The Domestic Abuse Project, as well as fundraiser for Women Against Rape and The Domestic Abuse Project.

She earned her Bachelor of Arts Degree in Business and Humanities from Golden Gate University and her Juris Doctor from Widener University School of Law.